Samuel from Granny & Grandad.
Christmas 1992

CASTLES

FACTS • THINGS TO MAKE • ACTIVITIES

RACHEL WRIGHT

Franklin Watts

London • New York • Sydney • Toronto

© Franklin Watts 1992

Franklin Watts
96 Leonard Street
London EC2A 4RH

Franklin Watts
14 Mars Road
Lane Cove
NSW 2066

UK ISBN: 0 7496 0761 0

Editor: Hazel Poole
Consultants: Dr. Michael Thompson, Brian Davison
Designed by: Sally Boothroyd
Artwork by: Jeremy Semmens
Photography by: Chris Fairclough
Additional picture research by: Juliet Duff

A CIP catalogue record for this book
is available from the British Library.

Printed in the United Kingdom

CONTENTS

SAFE HOUSES

During the Middle Ages — which lasted from about the 700s to 1500 AD — there were thousands of castles in western Europe. They were owned by the rich and powerful because only they could afford such splendid homes. Although many of these castles were never even threatened with attack, all were designed to repel the weapons of their day. They were like homely forts, built to protect their owner and his land, his family, his servants, his crafts people and his private army of knights.

CASTLE SITES

Where possible, castles were built on or near natural defences such as cliffs and coastlines. Many were founded near the port, town or crossroads they were designed to protect or control. Some were built near rivers and streams. A ditch could then be dug around the finished castle and the water diverted into it. These water-filled ditches, called moats, made castles much harder to attack.

▲ *This painting of Lusignan Castle in France is taken from the Duke of Berry's* The Book of Hours *which was made in 1400.*

▶ *Many wooden castles had gatehouses and moveable bridges to guard the main entrance and the approach to the tower.*

Castles were often closely linked with a neighbouring town or village. As well as being a rich man's home, they acted as a tax office, administration centre, courthouse and prison for local villagers.

WOODEN CASTLES

In some parts of Europe, the first castles were made of earth and wood. Often a steep-sided flat topped mound of earth was dug, surrounded by a ditch. A wooden tower was then built on top of the mound and encircled by a timber fence. This tower was the strong point of the castle and the place where valuables were kept.

The castle's owner and his family slept in apartments beside the Great Hall, in the courtyard below. The rest of the domestic buildings, including the kitchen, the chapel and the stables, also stood in the courtyard. These buildings were usually timber-framed and plastered over with earth and animal dung. The more important ones were roofed with tiles or shingles. The others were thatched with reeds or straw.

◄ *The castle at Peñafiel in Spain was built on top of a rocky ridge for protection. "Peña fiel" means "faithful rock."*

Wooden castles were cheaper, quicker and required less skill to build than stone ones, but they had two major disadvantages. They rotted and burned easily. For those who wanted a more permanent home, the only solution was to build in stone.

5

PULP AND PAPER CASTLES

1. Soak a sheet of newspaper in warm water. Squeeze the water out, and lay the paper flat on your baseboard.

▲2. Cover one side of the paper with wallpaper paste. Scrunch it up and knead it into a pulp. Repeat this process until you have enough pulp to model your castle's mound and courtyard. If you want to save time, mould your mound over an old plastic carton.

3. When your model is finished, leave it somewhere warm to dry.

TO MAKE A TOWER FOR THE MOUND

▲4. Fold a rectangle of corrugated card, as shown. Check that the outside ridges are vertical and that the four main panels are the same width.
Cut evenly spaced notches along the top of the tower, too.

TO MAKE THE ROOF

▲5. Draw a square with sides the same length as the width of one of the tower's panels. Add four tabs and cut this shape out.

6

▲**6.** Fold the tabs down and smear them with glue. Now fold the tower around its roof. Make sure that the roof lies below the notches. Glue the rest of the tower together and paint it.

TO MAKE THE COURTYARD BUILDINGS

▲**7.** Measure and mark a rectangle of corrugated card, as shown. The narrower panels must be the same width, as must the wider panels.

▲**8.** Following your markings, cut away the top of the card. Cover the tab with glue and bend the building into shape.

TO MAKE THE ROOF

9. Cut out a small piece of card. Fold it in half and glue it into place.

10. When you have made as many buildings as you need, paint them. Stick dried grass, straw or twine onto their roofs.

11. When it has dried, paint your model and arrange the castle's buildings on it. Cut strips of corrugated card for fences and glue them into position.

STONE STRONGHOLDS

No two castles built were ever exactly the same. Castle design varied according to where the castle was built, what it was built with, and who was in charge of its construction. Even so, like their wooden counterparts, many early stone castles were designed around one tall tower. These stone towers, later known as keeps, were the last retreat of the castle. They could be defended even if the thick curtain walls surrounding the castle had been breached.

The keep at Hedingham Castle in Essex is still standing, even though it was built in 1140. The cut-away picture below shows what it may have looked like when its lordly owner was home and entertaining important guests.

Because of the risk of fire, many castle kitchens were built in the courtyard instead of the keep.

9

WELCOME TO HEDINGHAM

The main door was on the first floor to keep it beyond the reach of enemies with battering rams. Just to be on the safe side, it was also protected by a small tower and a wood and metal grating, called a portcullis. When unwanted visitors arrived, the portcullis was slid down from above, to block the doorway.

Troublemakers ended up in the dungeon! They were probably lowered to their doom through a trapdoor in the ceiling.

ON THE GROUND FLOOR

The ground floor was the ideal place for storing food and drink because it was cool and dark. With no heating, and walls 3.5 metres thick, the temperature was always low.

Unlike some keeps, Hedingham's had only one well. As there were no pipes and taps, the water had to be carried to wherever it was needed. When someone wanted a bath, water had to be hauled upstairs, heated over a fire and poured into a large wooden tub.

THE SPIRAL STAIRCASE

A keep's floors were connected by a spiral staircase. Hedingham's stairs wind upwards to the right. This may have helped a descending soldier if he had to fight his way down the stairs.

THE CONSTABLE'S ROOM AND THE LORD'S APARTMENT

The constable, who was in charge of the running of the castle, lived with his servants on the first floor. Here he greeted visitors and sorted out day-to-day castle business.

The most magnificent room of all was the lord's apartment, on the second floor. This was the room he used to carry out his public duties and to entertain formally. Rich tapestries hung on the walls to give the room colour and help stop draughts.

Far less magnificent, however, were the draughty toilets called garderobes. These were tiny rooms with chutes which ran through the walls and out into a pit at the bottom. The keep's floors were covered with rushes and sweet-smelling herbs to try and hide the terrible smell coming from the garderobes.

UP ON TOP

The lord, his family and their personal servants slept in the most private room of all, on the top floor. However, if the king came to stay, he would have been given this room, and the lord would have been relegated to the floor below.

The higher floors had large windows because they were out of enemy and burglar reach. The lower floors had to have narrower windows, and arrow slits so that defending archers could fire out without enemy archers firing in.

MAKE YOUR OWN TAPESTRY

Tapestry in the Middle Ages was usually woven on a loom like this.

You will need: a piece of thick card ● scissors or craft knife ● pencil ● ruler ● threads, wool, string, raffia, strips of fabric, etc.

I. To make a simple loom, cut evenly spaced notches along the top and bottom edges of your piece of card.

▲**2.** Wind some wool onto the card and knot the ends to the outside notches. These are the warp threads. They need to be pulled fairly taut so that the card bends slightly.

▲**3.** To keep the edges of your tapestry straight, draw lines inside the first and last warp threads. These lines will help you to see whether you are pulling your weaving too tight.

A thread that weaves in and out of the warp is called the weft.

12

8. When you have finished, lift your weaving off its card loom. Slide a stick through the loops at the top and hang it up.

▲**4.** Tie your first weft to one of the outer warp threads. Weave it across the loom by going over and under alternate warp threads.

▲**5.** When you reach the final warp thread, weave the weft back again. This time it needs to go under and over alternately.

6. As you weave backwards and forwards, push the weft threads down firmly with your fingers. This will stop the warp showing through.

7. When you want to change colour or thread, knot the old and new weft threads together and push the knot to the back of your tapestry.

13

IN SEARCH OF THE PERFECT CASTLE

Castle design did not stop with the keep. As the Middle Ages progressed, many designers tried to keep attackers out of the castle courtyard by building stronger curtain walls. These walls had towers jutting out from them at fairly close intervals. This made it possible for archers to shelter in the towers and fire along the face of the wall.

Some of the larger wall towers were also turned into mini keeps. They provided extra accommodation and could be defended if the rest of the castle was captured.

A castle's weakest spot — its entrance — was also given a face lift. During the early 1200s, much mightier twin-towered gatehouses were built over the entrance. These gatehouses often had comfortable rooms upstairs where the constable in charge of the castle household might live.

The less welcoming entrance passage below was guarded by a drawbridge over the moat, wooden gates and at least one portcullis. "Murder holes" in the roof of the passage enabled defenders to drop missiles on the enemy, and to pour water on any fires they might have lit against the gates.

Sometimes the approach to a gatehouse was protected by a long narrow passage called a barbican. This made it difficult for large numbers of attackers to reach the gates or to smash through them with a battering ram.

A castle with such strong, well-protected outer walls and towers clearly had no need for a keep. Instead, the Great Hall, chapel, stores and kitchens were built inside the castle's courtyard, along with the rest of the domestic buildings. This arrangement gave everyone far more room than they would have had in a keep.

During the late 1200s, European castle designers started to build concentric castles. These had an open space at their centre and two sets of curtain walls. The inner wall overlooked the outer one. This enabled archers on the inner wall to fire at an approaching enemy over the heads of those defending the outer wall. If the enemy managed to cross the outer wall, he had no cover from the archers on the inner wall.

With every part defended by another part, concentric castles seemed almost impossible to capture.

▶ Beaumaris is Britain's finest concentric castle.

CREATE A CASTLE

Ask a grown-up to help you with this, as the knife blade will be sharp!

Card is easier to fold if it has been scored first. To do this, gently run the tip of your craft knife along the line you want to fold. Use a ruler when scoring straight lines.

TO MAKE THE GATEHOUSE

▲ 1. Cut out a rectangle of card. Divide it into four panels with a tab at one end and then score all four lines.

2. To make battlements, cut evenly spaced notches along the top of the card.

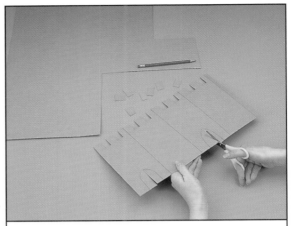

▲ 3. Cut a door into the bottom edge of the first and third panels.

▲ 4. Pierce a small hole into the left hand side of the second panel, and another into the right hand side of the fourth panel. The distance between each hole and its nearest panel must be the same. The distance between each hole and the base of the tower must also be the same.
The holes must be just big enough for a straw to fit through them.

5. Cover the tab with glue, fold the tower into shape and stick it together. Push a straw through both holes.

▲**6.** Cut out a small piece of card for the drawbridge. Use two tiny strips of sticky tape to attach it to the doorway furthest from the straw.

▲**7.** Thread a needle and knot the two loose ends of thread. Push the needle through one of the drawbridge's outer corners, and up through the front wall of the gatehouse.

▲**8.** Lower the drawbridge and gently pull the thread straight. Now tape the rest of the thread to the straw.
Make a second drawbridge rope in the same way.

9. Stick flattened strips of plasticine to the bottom of the drawbridge. It will now rise or lower when you turn both ends of the straw.

TO MAKE THE GATEHOUSE ROOF

▲ **10.** Measure the width of one of your gatehouse's panels. Draw a square with sides this same length onto some card. Add four tabs and cut the shape out.

11. Score the lines you've drawn. Fold the tabs down, smear them with glue and stick the roof into place.

TO MAKE WALL TOWERS

▲ **14.** Score the circle and cover its tabs with glue. Fold the tower around its roof and glue the two free edges together.

▲ **12.** Cut battlements along the top of a rectangle of thick paper. Roll the paper into a tube and hold it together with paper clips.

TO MAKE WALLS

▲ **13.** Stand the tower on another piece of thick paper and draw round it. Add tabs to your drawing and cut this shape out.

▲ **15.** Cut battlements along the top of a long length of card.

Cut another piece of card, as long as the first but not quite as tall.

Cut two strips of card. They must be the same length as your first piece of card, but only a quarter of its height.

▲ **16.** Mark tabs along the longer edges of both of the thinner strips of card. All the tabs must be the same width.

▲ **17.** Score all the lines you've drawn. Fold the tabs down, cover them with glue and stick all four lengths ▼ of card together, as shown.

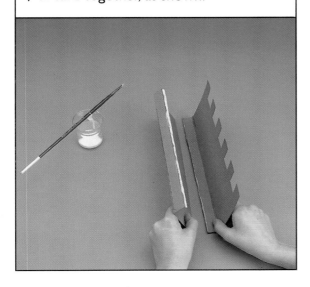

18. When you have made all the walls and towers you need, join them together with gummed paper. Tape two tall towers on either side of the gatehouse.

▲ **19.** Now paint your model. If you want the walls to look speckled, cover everything around the castle, including the floor, with newspaper. Dip an old toothbrush in watery paint, and run your thumb towards you along the bristles. The paint will spatter onto the walls.

TO MAKE THE DOMESTIC BUILDINGS

▲ **20.** Draw a line across the front of a small cardboard box. Then draw a diagonal line on each side of the box, as shown.
If the box has a lid, glue it shut.

▲**21.** Cut along these lines and lift up the flap. Now cut away the triangular areas on each side of the flap.

▲**22.** Straighten the flap and glue it onto the lower section of the box. You may find that you need to trim this roof.

23. To make a hall with two sloping roofs, simply glue two box buildings back to back.

24. When you have made as many buildings as you need, paint them.

TO MAKE A MOAT

▶**25.** Stand your castle walls on a large sheet of blue card. Draw a squiggly line around the edge of the card. Draw a line round the inner walls of the castle's courtyard, too.

26. Remove the card from under the castle and cut along both lines. To finish, slide your moat into place and arrange the domestic buildings in the courtyard.

Castles Under Attack

TRICKS AND SURPRISES

The best way to capture a castle was to take it by surprise. In 1204, a French soldier terrified the inhabitants of Château Gaillard by climbing up a garderobe chute and letting his comrades in through a window. Imagine the shock of going to the toilet late one night, only to find someone climbing out of the seat!

GOING OVER THE TOP

Where a surprise attack failed, a direct assault might succeed. If the castle had a ditch, log tracks had to be built across it so that attackers with ladders could scale the walls.

Those who favoured a safer approach climbed tall wooden towers, called belfries. These were wheeled up to the castle wall so that the soldiers inside could storm their way over.

GROUND LEVEL ATTACK

Attackers often tried to smash through a castle's gate or corner walls with a heavy metal-tipped tree trunk, called a battering ram. They also tried to batter down the castle's walls using mangonels and trebuchets.

The mangonel was powered by twisted ropes. It could hurl great weights, but not very accurately!

The trebuchet, on the other hand, was deadly accurate. Developed during the 1100s, it had a sling at one end and a heavy counterweight at the other. When the counterweight fell, the missile in the sling went hurtling towards its target.

A large trebuchet could throw a dead horse. Bombarding a castle with rotting remains helped to spread disease amongst the defenders. Being splattered by foul horse flesh can't have done much for their morale either!

GOING UNDERGROUND

Castles without water-filled moats were vulnerable to tunnelling. Enemy miners would tunnel under a wall, set fire to the wooden poles used to support the tunnel's roof, and then wait for both the tunnel and the wall above it to collapse.

A WAITING GAME

Attackers sometimes tried to starve their enemy into surrender by mounting a siege. They camped outside the castle and stopped food from being delivered.

Sieges were not always successful, though. A well-stocked castle could survive for months, and many attackers dared not leave their own castles undefended for that long.

23

FIRE YOUR OWN TREBUCHET

You will need: 2 blocks of balsa wood, 25mm square and 220mm long ● a large sheet of balsa (5mm thick) ● a stick of balsa wood about 220mm long ● unsharpened round pencil ● small screw hook ● matchbox ● string ● pebble ● sticky tape ● balsa cement ● craft knife ● small elastic band ● ruler ● paper.

Ask a grown-up to help you.

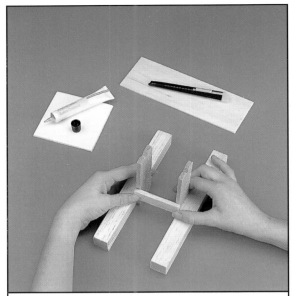

TO MAKE THE UPRIGHTS

1. Cut two pieces of balsa sheet, each measuring 110mm by 35mm. Carve a notch into one of the shorter sides of each piece. These notches must be wide enough and deep enough for the pencil to fit snugly into them.

▲3. Cut a piece of balsa sheet 70mm by 15mm, and glue it across the front of the uprights. The position of this bar will affect your trebuchet's firing range.

▲2. Glue the uprights onto your two blocks of balsa wood, as shown. Make sure the notches line up with each other.

▲4. Cut four pieces of balsa sheet, each 110mm by 20mm. Glue them, as shown, to complete the frame.

TO MAKE THE FIRING ARM

▲ **5.** Hold a pencil across your stick of balsa wood and fasten it with an elastic band. The pencil should be about a third of the way down the stick.

6. Tape a pebble to the short end of the arm. Glue half a matchbox tray to the other end.

▲ **8.** Screw a small hook into the back of the frame. Rest the arm on the uprights and pull it down so that you can slip the loop of string over the hook.

9. To fire your trebuchet, put a crumpled ball of paper into the matchbox and flick the string off the hook.

▲ **7.** Knot a length of string under the matchbox. Then tie a small loop in the string, near the knot.

CASTLES IN DECLINE

European castles went out of fashion because the society that had needed them began to change. In England and Wales this happened during the 1400s. As the monarchy grew stronger, private wars between great lords became less frequent. Pitched battles fought in the open countryside became more common. Since the two sides were often fighting to control the whole country, capturing a castle and its lands was not so important.

▲ *English gun fort, Deal, Kent.*

Coity Castle in Wales fell into disuse at the end of the 1500s. ▼

When cannons became popular weapons, soldiers were paid to man specially built gun forts. Fortress homes with their tall towers and arrow slits were no longer needed.

The times were changing in other ways, too. The nobility now longed for more comfortable homes, with bigger windows to let in more light. Some started to alter their castles accordingly. Others built grand manor houses instead. These new homes often had moats, battlements and gatehouses, but they were more for show than defence.

Castles that weren't adapted to a new role were abandoned. They were either pulled down and their building materials used for something else, or they were just left to crumble away.

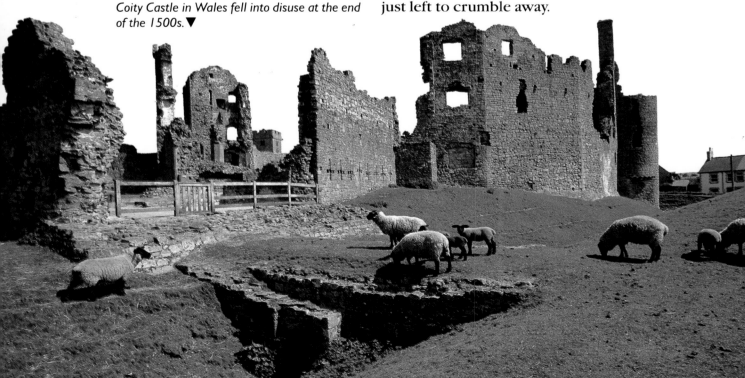

Castle building survived longer in Scotland, Ireland and other parts of Europe than in England and Wales. In fact, when cannons became effective siege weapons, some European castles were adapted to withstand their fire. Walls were thickened, towers were lowered and their flat roofs were used as cannon platforms.

However, as gunfire became more effective and central governments became more stable, castles in the rest of Europe fell out of favour, too. Rather than turn their homes into gloomy gun forts, the rich wanted to live in princely palaces and magnificent mansions.

▲ *François I of France began building this expensive palace at Chambord in 1519.*

During the 1700s and 1800s, fairytale like castles became fashionable in parts of Europe. But, unlike the genuine castles of old, these were built for beauty, not defence.

▶ *Neuschwanstein Castle in Germany was built in 1869-92 by "Mad" King Ludwig II.*

CASTLES IN THE AIR

Castles have not only fascinated those interested in the past. They have spellbound story tellers, too. European myths and legends are full of tales about castles. The gods of Norse mythology lived in Asgard. This was a castle kingdom in the air, guarded by a massive rainbow bridge. The Welsh sea god, Manawyddan the Wise, lived in a castle made out of human bones.

Celtic mythology has many stories about castles buried beneath the sea. One myth recalls the watery fate of the castle of Y's, in Cornwall. The people of Y's grew so unbelievably wicked that one day the sea rose up and swallowed their castle and town. They will only be saved when a young man on the mainland hears the sad sound of the castle's chapel bell.

As castles disappeared from the real world, story tellers started inventing more and more weird and wonderful ones to take their place. Some are dark and disturbing, like the devilish castle created by the Italian writer, Dante. In his castle, everything is horribly reversed. The moat is a river of death. The burning hot walls are designed to keep people in, not out. The curtain walls spiral inwards and downwards to a pit filled with horrors.

Some of the most popular stories of all have real castles at their centre. William Shakespeare's play *Macbeth* is set in Glamis Castle, in Scotland. His play *Hamlet* takes place at the royal castle of Elsinore, in Denmark.

Glamis Castle has a bloody history, both in fact and fiction. ▼

▲ Kronborg Castle in Denmark was made famous by the play Hamlet.

There is a German legend about a young man called Dietrich who rescues a princess from a dwarf king's castle, only to find that the ungrateful girl prefers her captor to him. The story goes that this castle can be found in the Tyrolean mountains. However, since only the pure and good can see it, it's unlikely that anyone has ever had a quick look inside!

GLOSSARY

Armourer — the man who looked after the castle's weapons and armour.

Barbican — some barbicans were like long walkways leading to the gatehouse. Others were like small gatehouses, built to protect the bridge leading to the main gatehouse.

Battering ram — a metal-tipped tree trunk or wooden pole, which was often suspended from the roof of a wooden shed on wheels. By swinging the ram to and fro against the castle's gate or corners, a team of men could smash their way through to the other side.

Battlements — a line of notches along the top of a tower or wall. Defending archers fired between the gaps, called crenels, and hid behind the higher bits of stonework, called merlons.

Belfries — tall wooden siege towers on wheels. They were often topped by a drawbridge and covered with animal hides for fireproofing.

Celts — an ancient race of people who came from western Britain, Wales, Ireland, Scotland and Brittany.

Château Gaillard — the favourite castle of King Richard I of England. It was built in the 1190s, on a cliff overlooking the River Seine, in France.

Curtain wall — general name given to the wall and towers surrounding a castle.

Legends — traditional stories that are part fact and part fiction. Myths and legends are handed down from one generation to the next.

Mangonel — a catapult used for throwing stones great distances when attacking a castle.

Myth — an ancient traditional story. Myths are often about gods and heroes. Many have a religious meaning, or try to explain some scientific fact.

Mythology — the study of myths; a collection of the myths and legends of a particular culture.

Norse mythology — the myths and legends of the Vikings, who came from Scandinavia.

Pitched battle — one that has been arranged and is fought on a chosen site.

Reed — a tall, stiff marsh or water grass.

Rushes — grass-like plants that grow near marshes.

Trebuchet — a large wooden catapult used when attacking a castle.

RESOURCES

PLACES TO VISIT

There are many castles in Britain open to the public. To find those nearest to you, contact your local tourist board or write to one of the following:

The National Trust (Headquarters)
36 Queen Anne's Gate
London SW1H 9AS

The National Trust for Scotland
5 Charlotte Square
Edinburgh

Cadw: Welsh Historic Monuments
Brunel House
Fitzalan Road
Cardiff CF2 1UY

Full details of all English Heritage castles, including opening times, are given in the Guide To English Heritage Properties. For your copy, write to:
English Heritage,
PO Box 43, Ruislip,
Middlesex HA4 0XW.
(enclose £1.95, plus 35p for postage).

Mountfitchet Castle in Stansted, Essex is a reconstructed 11th century timber castle. For further details, telephone 0279 813237.

For further information about Hedingham Castle, contact:
Castle Hedingham
Halstead
Essex CO9 3DJ
Tel: Hedingham (0787) 60261

BOOKS TO READ

Non Fiction
Castles by Jenny Vaughan, Franklin Watts 1984.

Inside story, A Medieval Castle by Fiona Macdonald and Mark Bergin, Simon and Schuster 1990.

See Inside a Castle by R. J. Unstead, Kingfisher Books 1986.

Medieval Castles by Brian Adams, Gloucester Press 1989.

Fiction
The Age of Chivalry, myths and legends, Cherrytree Books. (Myths and legends set in the age of castles).

Island of the Mighty: Stories of Old Britain by Hayden Middleton and Anthea Toorchen, Oxford University Press. (Re-telling of Welsh legends).

GAMES TO PLAY

You can get the following software from Rickett Educational Media, Ilton, Somerset TA19 9BR:

Fletcher's Castle — a Norman knight tries to build a timber castle in ten days.

Castle Under Attack — a strategy game for 9-14 year olds.

INDEX

Additional photographs: Bridgeman Art Library/Private Collection 4(b); Danish Tourist Board 29(t); Michael Holford 26(t), 27(t); Hutchison Library 4(t); Science Museum 12(t); Wales Tourist Board 14, 26(b); Zefa 27(b), 29(b).

The DK Art School

AN INTRODUCTION TO
OIL PAINTING

CONTENTS

CHARACTERISTICS OF OIL PAINT

ONE REASON WHY OIL PAINT has been so popular for hundreds of years is that it is an incredibly versatile painting medium which can be manipulated in many ways. Oil paint is so responsive because it dries slowly, allowing for colours to be modified and moved around on the surface of the painting for some time after they have been applied. This aspect of oil paint makes it an excellent medium for *alla prima* painting methods (pp.52-53), in which the paint itself can accurately reflect the immediacy of the artist's response to an image. Once oil paint has dried, it can be overpainted in a number of ways without the original colour beneath being disturbed or dissolved. This means that quite a complex layer structure of paint can be built up to create different effects.

A smooth board is overlaid with thin layers of transparent colour

Changing the texture of oil paint

If oil paint is used directly from the tube, it can be painted thickly with bristle brushes in a rich, impasted style. It has sufficient body to be able to maintain the crisp shape made by a brushstroke or a painting knife, whether urgent or delicate. This can give painting a real sense of directness, and establish an immediate link between the style of the painting and the artist. Oil paint can also be thinned down slightly to a creamy consistency, and brushed out to an enamel-like smoothness. If it is diluted very thinly with white spirit or turpentine, the consistency of the paint is ideal for sketching a composition, or formulated as a glazing

This rough board emphasizes the thick strokes of rich colour

colour if also mixed with an oil painting medium. The painting medium enables the glaze to become a transparent stain that modifies the appearance of a colour beneath. Oil paint can be used "stiffly", or unmixed, to create textured dry brush and scumbled techniques (pp.26-27) with bristle brushes, or it can be used in smoother manipulations with soft hair brushes. Of all the painting media, oil paint is the one best suited to blending techniques, in which one colour or tone can be made to fuse smoothly and almost imperceptibly into another.

The qualities of oil paint

One characteristic of oil paint that differentiates it from other media is its richness and depth of colour. This is because the pigments are ground in a drying oil that has a relatively high refractive index (the amount of light it reflects and absorbs). Chalk which otherwise appears opaque white becomes practically transparent when it is mixed with linseed oil. Pigments vary in their refractive index, which to a large extent dictates whether they appear transparent, semi-opaque, or opaque in oil. When compared to other media, oil paints are the most successful at exploiting the different qualities of opacity and transparency. Over a pure white ground, for example, a thin layer of a transparent oil colour has a saturation and depth that is difficult to achieve in another medium.

A rough coloured canvas gives these dry strokes of colour more texture

This fine canvas allows individual strokes of colour to be blended smoothly together

Creating different effects with oil paint

The four studies shown here demonstrate some of the characteristic effects of oil colour, used in different ways on a variety of surfaces. The smooth board on the top left-hand side provides a hard, untextured surface on which the brushstrokes remain clearly visible and unblended. A thin, warm transparent glaze, painted over the various colours, deepens the tone of the portrait and makes the face appear more cohesive. The bottom panel on the left has a rough surface on which thick paint has been applied as impasted brushstrokes. The uneven texture of this ground automatically affects each brushstroke, and as a result, the style is much bolder and chunkier. The top right-hand section is a rough canvas that has been prepared first with a single tone of one colour, applied over the whole surface and then left to dry. This coloured canvas is visible between areas of paint on the face and hair, so that both canvas and paint appear to be integrated as one surface. Paint has been applied with a dry brush technique that picks up the ridges of the rough canvas, while scratches (known as sgraffito) on the hair have been made with the end of a brush handle. The bottom right section shows a smooth canvas over which paint has been carefully blended. Different tones and colours have been painted as areas of light and shade, and then blended together to create a smooth transition between each colour.

A BRIEF HISTORY

THE DEVELOPMENT of oil paint as the most common medium for painting in Europe evolved slowly in the fifteenth century. Before this, a popular medium for painting on panel had been egg tempera, but it did not have the flexibility of pigments bound with a drying oil. Oil paint also had the capacity to be blended and manipulated on the surface of the painting and its transparency allowed for a far greater range of tones and resonant colours.

THE TRANSITION from egg tempera to oil paint in Northern Europe, and then in Italy towards the end of the fifteenth century, saw many examples of paintings in which the preliminary work was done in egg tempera, while later stages of painting, such as thin transparent glazes, were applied in oil colour. There are also examples of paintings in which egg and oil are contained in the same layer.

Although the Dutch van Eyck brothers are popularly credited with the discovery of oil painting in the early fifteenth century – Jan van Eyck *(b. before 1395-1441)* made progress developing the oil medium and using glazes – the use of oil-resin varnishes and drying oils is in fact quite well documented since the eighth century. Painters in Italy began to copy the Netherlandish way of modelling the underpainting in opaque colours, and then applying rich transparent glazes.

The progress of oil paint

Fifteenth-century Italy saw artists such as Piero della Francesca *(1410/20-92)*, whose early work is predominantly in egg tempera, coming to terms with the new oil medium. In Venice, Giovanni Bellini *(c.1430-1516)* began to exploit the depth and richness of tone and colour that could be had with oil

Jan van Eyck, *The Arnolfini Marriage,* 1434, *82 x 60 cm (32¼ x 23½ in) Oil has been used in this most famous of 15th-century portraits, though there may be egg tempera in the underpainting. With this new medium, van Eyck achieved an extraordinary range of tones, with deep shadows and clear bright lights.*

painting. He often worked first on an egg tempera underpainting, with its characteristic cross-hatched modelling, but the use of oil in the later stages of painting gave his figures an almost tangible existence. Perugino *(c.1445/50-1523)* and Raphael *(1483-1520)* were among other artists of the time working in both media. Raphael sustained the purity of the whites and blues in his skies by using the less yellowing walnut oil as a binding medium, rather than the linseed oil he used with other colours. By the

Cosima Tura, *Allegorical Figure,* mid-15th century, *116 x 71 cm (45¼ x 28 in) Said to portray one of the Muses, this Italian work was painted initially in egg tempera and then extensively re-modelled in oil. Transparent glazes enrich and deepen the coloured drapery.*

This painting shows Titian moving towards the very loose style of his last paintings, where fluidly modelled forms in opaque colours are overpainted in transparent glazes. The work is alive with movement, with the turbulent figure of Europa echoed in the twisting figures above.

first decade of the sixteenth century, oil paint had become universally established as the prime painting medium in Italy.

It is with later Venetian painters, such as Titian *(c.1487/90-1576)*, and then Tintoretto *(1518-94)*, that we see a freeing up of composition and expression. That these artists were now using oil paint exclusively had much to do with this new freedom of expression, for its flexibility allowed them to take a looser approach, not only in initial stages, but throughout the whole painting process.

Economical painting

By the seventeenth century, it was common for painters to work in an economical style on a coloured surface that provided the mid-tones, while opaque colours were added for lights, and thin transparent darks for shadows. Artists as diverse in style as Caravaggio *(1571-1610)* and Velazquez *(1599-1660)* used these dark "grounds" to emphasize any areas of high contrast and create dramatic lighting effects. Rembrandt *(1606-69)* often used double grounds on his canvases, with an underlayer of red bole (clay), or red ochre, and a layer of grey or brown on top. His images often seem to be sculpted in relief out of the dark ground. Rubens *(1577-1640)* worked similarly, but often prepared a warm yellow-brown layer which he applied with a bristle brush over a white priming. This underlayer helped him to create images more freely, giving more expression to his painting style.

Rembrandt van Rijn, *Self Portrait at the age of 63,* **1669,** *86 x 71 cm (33⅛ x 27¾ in)*
This painting was made in the last year of Rembrandt's life. The canvas was prepared with a dark brown ground, and the face modelled vigorously using thick Lead White. These impasted brushstrokes give vitality and texture to the face. There is a sense of composure and honesty in this self portrait, and the sense of gravity is heightened by the flickering shadows that cross his features.

Rachel Ruysch, *Flowers in a Vase, c.*1800,
57 x 43 cm (22½ x 17⅛ in)
Ruysch was an accomplished and successful still-life painter in 17th-century Holland. She adopted the popular technique of using a red-brown ground as a base, with opaque highlights and transparent darks on top. This ground has the effect of bringing the flowers out of their shadows and into bright focus. Each petal and leaf has been blended with exquisite finesse.

Unusual additions

Oil paintings from the seventeenth to the nineteenth centuries reveal some complex layer structures – and can include complicated materials. The British artist George Stubbs *(1724-1806)* used wax-resin mixtures with a drying oil in certain works. Some artists used what are now seen as unstable materials; Sir Joshua Reynolds *(1723-92)*, for instance, incorporated oil, resin, and bitumen mixtures into his paintings. Gainsborough *(1727-88)*, on the other hand, generally painted fairly thinly, with a drying oil plus pigment mixtures thinned with a solvent.

Research on paintings from the eighteenth and nineteenth centuries is limited, but what we can learn from the state of many works in this period is that the more straightforward the painting techniques and materials are, the more reliable the results.

A change of direction

During the nineteenth century, many artists rejected the constraints of traditional academic practices and moved towards *plein air* landscape painting from nature. This, combined with new ideas about colour and the discovery and development of new pigments, led to the new movement known as Impressionism. Artists such as Monet *(1840-1926)* and Renoir *(1841-1919)* made paintings that were often no less complex than oil paintings of the past, but were characterized by a sense of freshness and immediacy that was quite new. Now the character and texture of the individual brushstroke was integral to the look of the work. Colour became a focus of painting as never before, with new pigments available to artists and a greater use of bright, saturated primaries and secondaries.

The change in attitude and new approach to oil painting that was first initiated by the Impressionists led to further re-evaluations during the Post-Impressionist years of Gauguin *(1848-1903)* and Van Gogh *(1853-90)*. The Cubists Braque *(1882-1963)* and Picasso *(1881-1973)*, and German Expressionists Kirchner *(1880-1938)* and Nolde *(1867-1956)*, for example, all used the adaptable medium of oil to make great stylistic and technical changes in art. The Surrealists Max Ernst *(1891-1976)* and Salvador Dali *(1904-89)* both used oil in dramatic new ways. Dali re-worked the technique of blending oil into soft fluid forms to give expression to his interior thoughts and unconscious desires, while Ernst unlocked his imagination and invented or adapted techniques to give complex textural starting points for his works.

Claude Lorraine, *Echo and Narcissus*, 1644, *95 x 118 cm (46½ x 37¼ in) Like Titian, Claude incorporated stories from Ovid into his serene landscapes. While Titian's work is turbulent, Claude's is calm, suffused with a golden light. The poignancy of self-deception and the failure of human communication is underscored by this soft, warm Arcadian landscape.*

Claude Monet, *The Ducal Palace at Venice*, 1908, *81 x 98 cm (32 x 38½ in) Monet relied on colour contrasts to point up the brilliant effects of light. Pure yellows and violets and blues and orange-red make this facade glow against the sky and shimmer on the water.*

Paul Cézanne, *Green Apples*,
c.1873, *26 x 32 cm (10¼ x 12½ in)*
Cézanne's work differs from that of the Impressionists in its adherence to formal traditions of painting. He was unique in his use of colour and analytical approach to shapes. The warm orange-brown ground here contrasts with the cool, striking green apples.

Georgia O'Keeffe, *Red Canna*,
c.1923, *91 x 76 cm (36 x 29⅞ in)*
This is very different from the cool poise of Ruysch's work – O'Keeffe's flower is suffused with hot colour and is alive with feeling. The adjacent colours are simply blended, but together they form a stunning image.

Gerhard Richter, *Betty*,
1988, *102 x 72 cm (40⅛ x 28⅜ in)*
This portrait has a forceful power and intensity. The immaculate but engaging nature of the painted surface turns this image into something precious. In a world of millions of snapshots, Richter painstakingly retrieves one of them and asks us to look at it again carefully.

Twentieth-century style

With oil paint now used and adapted for a diversity of painting styles, its position at the forefront of painting media has been reinforced in the twentieth century. The German artist Gerhard Richter *(b. 1932)* has considered the relationship between painting and photography. His 1960s monochromatic paintings, based on newspaper photographs, exploited the way oil colour could be blended. He found a correlation between oil techniques and the smooth, often blurred quality of photographs.

During the most recent decades, many artists have found distinctive ways of working with this painting medium to give us new insights and meanings. Works by the Italian artists Francesco Clemente *(b. 1952)*, Enzo Cucchi *(b. 1949)*, and Mimmo Paladino *(b. 1948)*, although personal and individualistic, give expression to universal needs and aspirations. The cool, powerful works of British artist Lucien Freud *(b. 1922)* demonstrate the impact and intensity that can be achieved by painting directly from life, while the less direct approach of Howard Hodgkin *(b. 1932)* to his subjects has resulted in forceful works controlled by strong, energetic colour. Paintings by artists such as Christopher Lebrun *(b. 1951)* appear to draw on myths and images from the past, but they remain utterly contemporary in their engagement with surface, texture, and colour. In the USA and elsewhere in the world, a number of artists have begun to find inspiration in new forms of abstraction that still draw on the same techniques and traditions used for over five hundred years.

OIL PAINTS

OIL PAINTS ARE MADE BY GRINDING PIGMENTS with a drying or semi-drying vegetable oil such as linseed oil, walnut oil, safflower, or poppy oil. This oil binding medium gives the paint its characteristic appearance and distinctive buttery feel. Pigments ground in oil have a particular depth and resonance of colour because of the amount of light the oil reflects and absorbs. The oil also protects the pigment particles, as well as acting as an adhesive to attach the pigments to a painting surface. Commercial manufacturers add to this basic mix to give a range of stable paints with relatively consistent drying times.

Walnuts

Walnut oil
Walnut oil was more popular in the past than it is today, as it is difficult to keep in tubes for any length of time. Walnuts contain about 65% oil.

Poppy seeds

Opium poppy plant

Poppy oil
Poppy seeds contain about 50% oil. This semi-drying oil is slow to dry in comparison with drying oils such as linseed oil, so to avoid any cracks appearing, ensure it is completely dry before overpainting.

Drying and semi-drying oils
The range of drying and semi-drying oils used to bind pigments together are made from the crushed and pressed seeds of certain plants. The most important of these plants is linseed oil, which is a golden yellow drying oil and comes from the seeds of the flax plant. The best quality linseed oil is cold-pressed, although most modern oils are hot-pressed. Poppy oil is a semi-drying oil made from the seeds of the opium poppy plant. It is a pale straw colour and has long been popular as a binding medium for pale pigments that might

be affected by the more yellowing linseed oil. It is popular for alla prima work (*see* pp.52-52) as it takes a long time to dry. This means that the paint can be moved around for some time after it has been applied. Safflower oil from the seeds of the safflower plant is similarly pale and slow-drying and it can be used in the same manner as poppy oil. Walnut oil from the nuts of the walnut tree was very popular in the past for its pale colour, and it has been identified as a binding medium for white and blue pigments in many Renaissance paintings. It should be used fresh as it goes rancid quickly.

Traditional and modern oil mixes
In the past, artists used a wide variety of ingredients in their painting mediums (below) which caused pictures to darken and crack. Nowadays a mix of stand (linseed) oil and turpentine is recommended, and very little resin, if any, should be added.

Sun-bleached linseed oil

Copal oil varnish

Black oil

Orpiment pigment

Realgar pigment

Azurite pigment

Azurite

Realgar

Orpiment

Traditional pigment sources
Traditional pigments were made from natural sources. The mineral azurite was ground to powder and used as an underlayer for Ultramarine Blue. The red and yellow pigments realgar and orpiment are poisonous and no longer available. Synthetic substances now replace many natural pigments.

Oil absorption

If pigment particles were the same smooth shape, size, and weight, they would use the same amount of oil to coat their surfaces. In fact pigments each need a specific amount of oil to reach a desired uniform consistency. Paint with less oil content is less flexible and is liable to crack if you paint it over a colour with high oil absorption. This can be avoided using the "fat-over-lean" rule (see pp.58-59).

Low oil content *(50% or less)*
Only a few pigments are included here; Ultramarine (above), Manganese Blue, and Flake White.

Medium oil content *(50-70%)*
Cadmium Yellow, Cadmium Red (above), Raw Umber, Oxide of Chromium, and Ivory Black are included in this category.

High oil content *(70% or more)*
Pigments include Burnt Sienna, Raw Sienna (above), Burnt Umber, Winsor Blue and Green, Alizarin, Permanent Rose, and Cobalt.

Mixing oil paints

Making your own oil paints is not difficult. You need a ground glass slab and a flat-bottomed glass muller (these are also available in a hard stone such as granite), a large palette knife, cold-pressed linseed oil, and some pigment powder. Avoid using toxic pigments such as Lead White or Cobalt Blue as they are too dangerous. You should use a dust mask whenever you grind powder colours.

Materials

Airtight jar

Palette knife

1 ▲ Place a small heap of pigment powder in the centre of a glass slab and make a well in the middle of the powder. Then pour a small amount of linseed oil into the well.

2 ◀ Use the palette knife to mix the oil and pigment into a stiff paste. You may find this is easier to do with some pigment powders than with others.

3 ◀ Place the muller on top of the paint mixture and start to grind it with a continuous smooth circular action. Use the palette knife to scrape any paint from the edge of the muller and the sides of glass slab back into the middle.

4 ▲ When the paste has achieved a creamy consistency, scrape it off and store it in a small airtight jar.

Glass slab and muller

Modern commercial paints

Commercial oil paints are sold in tubes, and most manufacturers produce two ranges; artists', and students'. Artists' paint is of a higher quality as it contains the best pigments and has the highest proportion of pigment to drying oil. The price of individual colours largely depends on the cost of the raw material used to obtain that particular colour. The wide range of cheap, bright, lightfast synthetic pigments now available are a good option.

Cadmium Red is a lightfast opaque colour that was introduced in the early twentieth century.

Transparent artificial Ultramarine replaced the natural pigments made from lapis lazuli in the nineteenth century.

EQUIPMENT

OF THE EQUIPMENT YOU NEED for oil painting, the most important tools are your brushes, and the look of a painting depends on their quality. There are two main types of brushes: stiff hair bristle brushes made from hog hair, and soft hair brushes made from sable or synthetic material. You also need a certain amount of solvent, such as turpentine or white spirit, to dilute your oil colours and to clean off excess paint. Linseed oil, the basic binding medium for oil paint, can also be used to modify the consistency of colours. You can paint on many different surfaces and textures, but those used most frequently by oil painters are canvases and wooden panels. Keep equipment clean and always screw the lids back on bottles of solvent as they are a serious health hazard.

Bristle brushes

Synthetic brush

Sable brush

Toe (tip) of brush

Heel of brush

Ferrule

Palette knife

Protective plastic case

Brushes
Bristle brushes are mainly used for oil painting as they move the paint around on the textured surface of a canvas with ease. Soft hair brushes are good for small details and smooth effects. Oil painting brushes traditionally have long handles. Store your brushes safely when you aren't working with them.

Linen canvas

Primed canvas board

Wooden panel

Painting surfaces
You can paint on almost any surface, including stone, glass, and metal. The materials most commonly used are canvases and wooden panels such as plywood, hardboard, and fibreboard. Commercially produced oil paper is good for trying out ideas and techniques.

Palette and painting knives
Palette knives are indispensable for moving paint around on a palette and cleaning it off. Painting knives, on the other hand, are used for applying paint and have a differently shaped blade and handle.

Painting knives

Dippers
These containers store small amounts of solvent and painting medium on a palette.

MAHL STICK

If you need a steady hand to work on a particular area, use a mahl stick. A mahl stick is a piece of light bamboo, about 1.25m (4ft) long, with a ball-shaped end covered in soft chamois leather. You can make your own mahl stick if you prefer.

Modern palettes

Use a palette to mix your colours. You can make your own palette from plywood by sanding it down and sealing it with linseed oil. Alternatively, you can use a glass slab over a piece of paper, or a disposable paper palette.

Disposable paper palettes

EASELS

There are a variety of easels available from artists' suppliers, from the simple sketching easel that folds right up for easy carrying on location, to the heavy studio easels that can hold large paintings comfortably. Some artists like to work on paintings suspended on nails on a studio wall, or propped up on a table, but it makes sense to have a good adjustable easel for your work.

Vertical studio easel

Sketching easel

Radial studio easel

Mahogany palette

This kidney-shaped mahogany palette, with its characteristic dark red-brown colour, was originally developed for artists who worked on a similarly coloured painting surface. This meant colours on the palette could be seen as they would look on the painting.

HEALTH HAZARD

Solvents can damage your health – screw the lid on after use and keep your studio well ventilated.

Solvent

You need to use a certain amount of solvent to dilute your colours and clean your equipment. Use either white spirit or turpentine.

Drying oil

Linseed oil is the basic medium for binding coloured pigments and drying them when painted. Use it to modify the consistency of paint.

Oil painting medium

This enhances the consistency and glossiness of oil paint. If you don't want to buy it, mix refined linseed oil, or stand oil, with turpentine.

Varnish

Varnishes are designed to protect a painting and give it a matt or a gloss finish. Dammar varnish and ketone varnish are recommended.

CHOOSING COLOURS

MOST ARTISTS LEARN about colour by discovering how it works in practice. Painting is a constant process of individual experimentation and discovery, and it is unlikely that any two artists would work with the same colours. It is, however, helpful to look at some of the basic theories of colour in relation to oil painting.

Ideally, artists would need only the primary colours of red (magenta), yellow, and blue, plus white, to mix any colour. In reality it can be difficult to find suitable pigments of the purity that allow, for instance, the same yellow to make a pure orange with red, and a pure green with blue. Use instead a limited palette of versatile colours.

Colour wheel
This colour wheel shows the three primaries, red, yellow, and blue, and the three secondary colours in between that are made by mixing two of the primaries. The wheel also shows the two main methods of mixing oil colour; the paint has been mixed opaquely on the outside wheel, and transparently on the inside wheel.

These colours have been painted very thinly, or transparently, over a white surface which shows their true colour, and not as they appear when squeezed out of a tube.

Opaque colours, with their rich, well-bodied appearance, conceal the surface they are painted on. Transparent colours can be made to look opaque by adding white paint.

Adjacent colours
Adjacent colours have some similarity in hue (the actual colour of an object or substance). Green contains blue in its mix, which gives these hues an automatic link. On a colour wheel with a wider range of colours, adjacent colours are those that are positioned next to one another.

Complementary colours
Pairs of colours situated opposite each other on the colour wheel give maximum contrast and enhance one another to appear brighter.

Warm and cool colours
Reds are usually thought of as warm, and blues cool. In fact, depending on their hue and context, colours can be warm or cool. Here one red (left) is cool and the other red warm. It is important to know this when mixing colours, as the cool red makes a better violet if mixed with blue.

Arranging your palette
When you choose a palette of colours, try to include both a warm and a cool colour of each hue, or a versatile colour such as Winsor Blue. There are no set rules for laying out your colours, but it makes sense to place adjacent colours next to one another and to keep white paint separate.

The top six colours are mainly primary colours, combining opaque and transparent paints, and placed in the order of the colour spectrum.

The paints along the side include naturally opaque earth colours and more muted, low-key colours.

Keep white paint slightly separate as it will be used mainly for lightening other colours.

Transparent and opaque colours

It is important to understand the difference between opaque paint, which conceals the surface it is painted on, and transparent paint, which appears dark in a tube but transparent when painted thinly on a white surface. The transparent Permanent Rose shown here has been thinned gradually to show its true colour, and then mixed with white to give opaque "tints". Black is then added to give a range of different "shades".

Permanent Rose, thinned down to its true colour

If white paint is added, a range of opaque tints is produced

Touches of black mixed into the paint give dark shades

Recommended colours

The limited range of opaque [O] and transparent [T] colours (right) gives an extremely flexible palette, but add more colours if you wish. Recommended are all Cadmium and Mars colours, Light Red, Azo Red, Alizarin Crimson, Venetian Red, and Winsor Red, Arylamide or Azo Yellow, Manganese Blue, Cerulean Blue, Ultramarine Blue, Cobalt Blue, and Indanthrone Blue. Quinacridone (Violet), Dioxazine Violet, and Cobalt Violet are also good, as are Cobalt Green, Viridian, Terre Verte, Raw Sienna, Burnt Sienna, Flake White, Zinc White, Lamp Black, and Ivory Black.

Permanent Rose [T]
(Quinacridone Red)

Cadmium Red [O]

Cadmium Yellow Pale [O]

Transparent Gold Ochre [T]

Winsor Green [T]
(Phthalocyanine Green)

Winsor Blue [T]
(Phthalocyanine Blue)

Titanium White [O]

Oxide of Chromium [O]

Yellow Ochre [O]

Indian Red [O]

Burnt Umber [T]

Mixing primaries

It is easy to assume that a mixture of two colours will simply produce a single third colour. In fact, the two colours together can produce many versions of the third colour, in a wide range of tones. A useful exercise is to try painting a simple still life, such as the one below, using a range of tones in a secondary colour that you have mixed from two primaries.

1 ▲ Before you paint these peppers, use a small scrap of card and mix a range of different oranges from Permanent Rose and Cadmium Lemon (*below*). Then, with a clean medium-sized filbert bristle brush, paint the red pepper with shades of orange on a piece of oil paper.

Mix a range of orange tones before painting

Primary Peppers

These peppers look like real objects rather than flat images because a variety of different tints and shades create dimension and shape on each object. This range of clean orange tones has been achieved by carefully mixing different quantities of the primary colours, red and yellow.

PURE COLOURS

Use two jars of white spirit to first clean off excess paint, and then rinse the brush. This will retain the purity and strength of each colour you use.

2 ◀ Use lighter tints of orange or yellow for highlights, and darker shades of orange or red for areas in shadow. The lightness or darkness of each orange mix creates a "tone" which models and shapes the peppers so they appear three-dimensional.

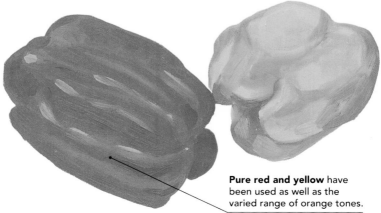

Pure red and yellow have been used as well as the varied range of orange tones.

COLOUR MIXING

WHEN YOU DECIDE to paint with a particular colour, you have a choice of how you mix it and apply it to a painting surface. There are two principle ways of mixing colours. Firstly, you can mix together one colour with another physically on a palette (*see below*), but you should always add small touches of the darker colour to the lighter one so that you do not make more of the mixture than you need. A positive feature of oil paint is that the colour you mix and apply wet has the same tone when it dries. Secondly, you can overlay one colour on to another. A thin film of transparent red paint over a dry layer of yellow will give an orange colour that looks quite different to a physically mixed orange. Another method of colour mixing is to place small dots of pure colour side by side. These appear to combine "optically", or visually, in the viewer's eye so that a third colour is perceived.

Mixing clean colours

When you mix colours together, always mix them away from other paints on the palette to prevent the original colours becoming sullied. If you physically mix colours (right), use a clean palette knife or brush to transfer colour each time. The brush must again be completely clean before you overlay paint (below). You can also mix colours in a "striated" brushstroke, with separate colours on a brush (below right). To mix colours optically, gauge the right proportion of one colour to another, or you will create something that looks grey. Allow one set of dots to dry before adding a new colour.

1 ▲ Lay paints around the edge of your palette with a good gap between them so they stay clean. Use a palette knife to transfer colours away.

2 ▲ To physically mix green from these two colours, start with the yellow and add small dabs of the stronger blue paint to it as you mix.

3 ▲ Continue to add touches of blue to the mix until you have the right shade of green. Make sure that both paints are thoroughly mixed together.

Dots of yellow and blue blend visually

A striated brushstroke contains two separate colours that give the impression of a third

CARE OF PAINTS

Paints are expensive, so it is worth looking after your materials. Clean excess paint away with a tissue so that the lid screws on firmly. This also protects the strength and purity of a colour, which can easily be ruined if the tube is neglected.

Yellow painted stiffly over blue gives a broken green

A thin film of yellow over blue appears green

THE SIMPLE COLOUR MIXING exercise on this page concentrates on mixing the actual colour of objects in a still life. However, the colours are mixed in a variety of ways to achieve certain effects. Strokes of individual colour are optically mixed or overlaid, while a touch of white added to the dark, transparent paint Winsor Blue gives a rich, deep opaque blue for the cloth.

1 ▶ Begin by sketching the outline of each object, and then fill in the shapes with colour. Paint a layer of pure Winsor Blue on the pepper, and physically mix an orange colour for the onion. The jug is opaque, so add some Titanium White to this mixture.

2 ▲ When the blue paint on the pepper has dried, overlay it with a separate layer of pure Cadmium Yellow, dabbed on with a small clean filbert brush. You should find that although touches of blue will show through, the resulting effect will make the pepper look green.

3 ◀ Use a small round brush to paint strokes of Cadmium Red and Cadmium Yellow on the onion. Keep the paint quite thick so that the colours look as strong and as pure as possible.

4 ▶ Paint a thin mix of Winsor Blue over the cloth so that it deepens the colour of the material and describes areas of shadow.

Still Life Study

This study shows how many options there are to mixing colours, and the different effects they make. Separate strokes of strong colour on the onion appear to merge into a vivid orange, while the jug has been painted with physically mixed colours that give a more subtle appearance. Although the pepper has been overlaid with paint, any touches of individual colour still visible help to establish areas of light and shadow.

This jug has been painted with a physically mixed opaque colour which gives it a strong, solid look.

A layer of yellow over thin blue paint gives this pepper a fresh appearance.

Individual strokes of yellow and red appear to blend optically to give an orange colour.

A thin film of transparent blue deepens the tone of the cloth.

Sharon Finmark

LOW-KEY & HIGH-KEY COLOUR

LOW-KEY PAINTINGS are usually defined by their subdued tones and colour mixtures that tend towards neutral browns and greys. High-key paintings are exactly the opposite, with simple mixtures of pure, bright, saturated colours, often mixed with white. The strong distinction between high and low-key painting needs to be made to enable us to focus our use of colour in terms of our approach to subject matter. Many paintings contain elements of each, but certain subjects lend themselves well to the use of high-key or low-key colour. These simple exercises show how easily the mood of a subject can change.

LOW-KEY PAINTINGS are often created with tertiary colours (a mixture of three or more colours), such as the Payne's Gray above. These can produce neutral, unsaturated hues. Some artists use a small range of neutral colours that are similar in mood and tone, but their paintings can vary enormously in atmosphere. This means that a work may be low in key and sombre in mood, but it can either be a quiet reflective study suffused with a subtle atmosphere, or painted in a dramatic way on a dark ground. Some subjects are by their nature low-key, such as moonlit scenes or dimly lit interiors, but almost any subject can be treated in a low-key manner.

1 ▲ Block in main areas of the composition using a large brush and mixes of opaque green, blue, and Payne's Gray, thinned with turpentine. Paint with loose brushstrokes to keep the composition simple.

2 ▶ Paint over the first layers of colour with thicker opaque paint that has been mixed with a little oil painting medium. Use a medium-sized flat brush to capture the shape of the fish most effectively.

3 ◀ When the tone and depth of the composition is complete, add finer details and opaque highlights with a small round brush. Keep the highlights soft and subtle and without harsh lines.

Gutted Mackerel
This painting is composed of subdued, almost neutral colours that create a soft light and a gentle atmosphere.

A limited palette of colours keeps the work more powerful and controlled.

Opaque highlights help to create a subtle movement through the painting.

Elaine Halden

Payne's Gray

Cobalt Blue

Cerulean Blue

Cadmium Red

Burnt Umber

Yellow Ochre

Cadmium Yellow

BRIGHT, SATURATED colours such as the Cerulean Blue left, produce high-key works that are light and optimistic in tone, but which can also be richly textured. High-key scenes are usually painted on white or near-white grounds which illuminate thinly applied colours to achieve high-key effects. Transparent high-key paints can be used opaquely by adding a little white paint to bring the colour out.

1 ▶ The white surface of this panel helps to keep the colours that are painted over it as bright and as luminous as possible. Paint the first coats of thin mid toned colour with a medium-sized filbert brush. Keep the colours as pure and as intense as possible.

2 ▲ Use a smaller brush and a mix of Manganese Blue, Cerulean Blue, and Viridian, together with a touch of Titanium White, to strengthen the bright but cool colour of the plate.

3 ◀ Paint bright markings on top of the initial thin layers of colour to give the fish better definition. The first layers of individual colour should have created a sufficient sense of shape and tone on each fish.

4 ▶ As the composition is built up, less white paint is mixed into each colour so that the last layers look transparent and strong. Add final highlights of thick, stiff white paint with a medium-sized or small brush.

Parrot Fish
This work has bright, saturated colours, mixed mainly from primaries and secondaries, so that they retain their purity and strength.

Strong saturated colour produces a heightened, vibrant atmosphere.

Complementary colours enhance one another to make the painting appear even more luminous and strong.

Jane Gifford

Viridian Green   *Ultramarine Blue*   *Manganese Blue*

Cerulean Blue   *Raw Sienna*   *Magenta*

Permanent Rose   *Cadmium Red Pale*   *Yellow Ochre*

Cadmium Yellow   *Lemon Yellow*

GALLERY OF COLOUR

IF YOU TURN THE COLOUR CONTROL switch on your television set, you can make an image change dramatically from black and white through a range of colour effects to brilliant, saturated colour. When you paint, you are faced with a similar range of choices and dramatic effects. Your decisions about colour should be affected by the nature of your subject and by the way you see it and want to describe it. Colour can convey a mood or create an area of special focus. By placing one colour next to another, or choosing one particular colour rather than another, you can change the visual and emotional impact of a painting. Use colour to say what you want, as well as what you actually see.

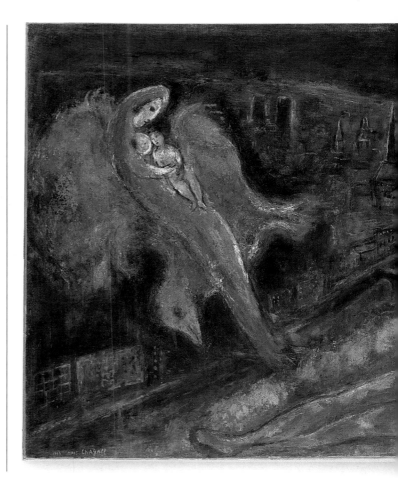

Frederick Gore RA,
Bonnieux at Cherry Time, **1989,** *66 x 52 cm (26 x 20 in)*
Gore has used what seem unnaturally bright primary and secondary colours for this study. But he has captured the presence and feel of this French village far more accurately than if he had matched the colours carefully. Bright high-key colour has been used to generate a feeling of warmth and spontaneity, which gives the work a strong impact.

This detail shows how saturated yellows complement cooler lilacs and purples to heighten an effect of brilliant sunshine on the scene.

Lively, loose brushwork adds sparkle to the composition and gives the painting more of an immediate quality.

Marc Chagall,
Bridges over the Seine,
1954, *112 x 163 cm (44 x 64 in)*
*Chagall's painting demonstrates
how colour establishes a particular
mood or atmosphere. Above the
cool dark city hovers a magenta
and purple bird that seems to
provide a haven for the woman
and her child. The orange-red of
these figures supported within the
bird's wings generates a warm focal
point for the work. Below, in the
cool, calm blue of the foreground,
a couple sleeps beneath this bright
vision. The green goat, adjacent
to the blue and complementing the
magenta, provides a colour link
between all the components of
the composition, and the harmony
of strong colours is intensified
by the dark background.*

The colour harmony in this
detail is created by using
colours that are adjacent to one
another on the colour wheel.

Philip Sutton RA,
P.S. as Don Quixote, **c.1989,** *70 x 70 cm (27 x 27 in)*
*Sutton has retained a clarity and purity of colour in this
work by having made clear decisions before painting about
where particular colours will go. The lack of overpainting
also keeps the colours clean. The painting relies on flat shapes
rather than three-dimensional forms to keep the image strong:
the bold blue shape defining the hair and beard encloses
the complementary orange-reds of the face. This intensifies
the colour in the face and separates it from the background
colour, making it a focal point. It also contrasts with the bird
in red and yellow, perched delicately on the man's hat.*

Elaine Halden, ***Mushrooms,*** *46 x 53 cm (18 x 20½ in)*
*This low-key study is painted with a subdued palette, yet it
retains a fresh appearance. The vegetables are painted with
economy, while a hint of pink in the garlic and ochre in the
mushrooms add subtlety to the colour effect. The white
circle of the plate gives the work a slightly formal quality.*

Bernadette Kerr, ***Scalinata,*** *85 x 96 cm (33½ x 37½ in)*
*The soft, almost abstract, forms in this painting are created
with a limited range of warm ochres and terracottas and
cool, muted blue-greens. Colours are unsaturated and used
opaquely, and in some areas they have been mixed with
white to produce a range of pale, low-key tints.*

23

BRUSHES

This special cleaner suspends brushes in turpentine

THE BRUSHES YOU USE soon become a matter of personal choice and when you have been painting for some time, you will begin to recognize exactly which brush you need to use for a particular area of your painting. Bristle brushes are used for large-scale work, impasto work, and more vigorous techniques. They are excellent for laying in large areas of flat or blended colour. Sable or synthetic soft hair brushes should be used for more precise work with oil paint mixed to a creamy consistency. As you use your brushes you will find that they often become worn in a way that suits your style and once they lose their spring and paint-carrying capacity, they may become suitable for other techniques, such as vigorous dry brush techniques (*see* pp.26-27).

Round brushes

Size 10 round hog hair brush

Size 12 round synthetic brush

Size 2 round sable brush

Smooth strokes
Round brushes have smooth, curved ends and can be used for long, continuous strokes of colour. Larger sizes have a good paint-carrying capacity, while the smaller sizes are less effective at holding paint. Small soft hair rounds taper to a fine point and are useful for the final stages of a painting or for adding in precise details.

Square brushes

Size 8 short flat hog hair brush

Size 10 short flat synthetic brush

Size 7 long flat sable brush

Rectangular marks
Flat brushes with short hairs can be used for applying small dabs of colour. Longer-haired flats carry enough paint to make long clean-edged strokes of colour. The thin edge of the brush can also be used to make sharp lines.

Filbert brushes

Size 10 long filbert hog hair brush

Size 6 long filbert hog hair brush

Versatile brushwork

Filberts are made as round brushes with the ferrule then flattened so that although the hairs are flat, they retain their rounded points. They combine some of the best features of flats and rounds, making rounded dabs of paint and strong lines of colour.

Size 5 short filbert synthetic brush

Specialized brushes

Hog hair fan blender

Modifying the paint

A fan blender, or duster, is used for more particular techniques and to modify paint that has already been applied to a surface. The brush is used dry to soften edges or eliminate visible brushstrokes to give a very smooth appearance. It can also be used for delicate brushstrokes, such as adding highlights to hair.

BRUSH CARE

It is important to wash your brushes at the end of a painting session or they can be damaged permanently. If you leave them standing in a jar of turpentine, the pressure will distort the hair. Never use hot water to clean the brushes, as it may expand the metal ferrule and cause the hairs to fall out.

1 *Remove excess paint from the brush by cleaning it carefully with a cloth or a piece of kitchen towel that has been dipped in turpentine.*

2 *Dip the brush into a jar of turpentine and clean it thoroughly, pressing the tip of the brush against the base if paint still needs to be dislodged from the hairs or the ferrule.*

3 *Wipe the brush again on a clean part of the cloth to remove the last of the excess paint.*

4 *Use washing up liquid or soap to work up a lather with the brush in the palm of your hand.*

5 *Rinse the brush under a running tap of cold or warm water, making sure you remove all the washing up liquid completely and there is no trace of the pigment. Shake off the water and reshape the tip of the brush with your fingers. Store the brush upright in a suitable jar.*

BLENDING & DRY BRUSH

OIL PAINT IS ONE of the most adaptable painting mediums and you can create many effects with it. There are several techniques for manipulating paint on a surface with a brush; blending, dry brush and scumbling, glazing, and impasto. Blending gives a smooth transition between colours, while dry brush and scumbling break up the paint to create texture.

Use a clean dry brush to blend separate colours. Make each gentle brushstroke in the same direction.

Smooth objects
The hard, polished appearance and smoothly rounded surface of this cup is accentuated by careful blending.

Blending
The one feature that marks oil paint out from other painting media is its ability to be blended. Separate tones and colours can be painted on to a surface adjacent to one another and then blended by stroking a clean brush down the join between them. Blending may involve slightly softening the sharp outline of an object against a background, or working on a whole painting so that it takes on a rounded, seemingly three-dimensional effect. Use soft hair brushes for small-scale work and bristle brushes for large areas.

Realistic effects
This painting shows how oil colour can be blended after it has been applied to a surface. The features of this woman's face have been modelled to give a subtle effect, shown by the smooth tonal change between the highlight on her left cheek through to her hairline and the smooth gradation of tone in her shirt sleeve. Tiny areas, such as the iris of her eye, also rely on smooth transitions between separate areas of colour.

Both large and small areas of colour in this painting have been blended smoothly together to create a soft, realistic sensation.

Dry brush and scumbling

Dry brush involves scrubbing a small amount of "dry" paint thinly over a surface with a bristle brush. One way of achieving this dry quality is to load a brush with colour and wipe it on a rag before painting. Dry brush creates a broken colour effect, in which indentations or dips in the texture of a surface remain free of colour, while the raised areas pick it up. This gives a "half tone" effect, mingling a light tint (the white of the surface), with a darker shade (the colour of the paint). Scumbling is the technique of painting over a dry layer of colour using a dry brush effect, so that the colour below shows through intermittently.

Scumbling is most effective when light colour is laid over dark paint with a bristle brush.

Creating texture
The furry body of this teddy bear is suggested by scumbling a semi-opaque cream colour over a deep shade of ochre paint.

A thin mix of blue paint over the large area of the sky picks up the rough texture of this coloured canvas to produce a half tone effect.

The dry brush effects in this painting create an interesting visual sensation. Areas of broken paint on the rough canvas produce a series of half tones that echo the rough, barren look of the landscape.

Texture in a landscape
Dry brush or scumbling can give a painting a lively appearance, accentuating the impact of colours and textures. In this work, simple mixtures of colours in different tones have been used to define the broad shapes of a landscape. These mixtures have been dry brushed into the weave of the canvas so that the image seems to be almost imprinted on to the surface. The matt colour effects in clear, slightly shaded tones heighten the simple painting style. There is a lack of extraneous detail which, together with the absence of human figures, helps to maintain the textural quality and dreamlike atmosphere of this scene.

GLAZING & IMPASTO

GLAZING IS A USEFUL WAY of enriching or deepening the tone of a colour. A glaze is a thin layer of transparent oil colour that is applied over an existing area of dry paint. The colour is generally mixed first with an oil painting medium which helps to adapt its consistency and increase its transparency. A glaze can also serve as a form of colour mixing (*see* p.18),

A glaze enriches another colour

so that a thin red glaze over a layer of dried yellow paint produces an orange colour quite different in appearance to a physically mixed orange. Impasto, on the other hand, is a technique of applying a colour very thickly so that a surface retains the character and shape of each brushstroke. Oil paint has a good viscous quality suitable for impasto, so it is usually applied straight from the tube with a painting knife or a bristle brush. Impasto produces a fresh, vigorously textured look.

Glazing

Glazing can be used for a number of colour effects as its transparent quality allows the layer of paint underneath it to remain visible. Several successive layers of rich transparent glazes can achieve a wonderfully deep, luminous effect in a painting. A glaze also brings a particular unity and harmony to a work with its uniform covering. The paint should be mixed with an oil painting medium (a mixture of stand oil and white spirit or turpentine) until it forms a puree-like consistency, and then applied to the surface of a painting with a soft hair or bristle brush. Once the glaze has been applied it can be smoothed into an even layer over the surface using a clean dry round brush. For large areas a shaving brush is useful (*see* p.58). Before glazing, always make sure the existing paint layer is dry.

The glaze is painted thinly so that the colour beneath can show through.

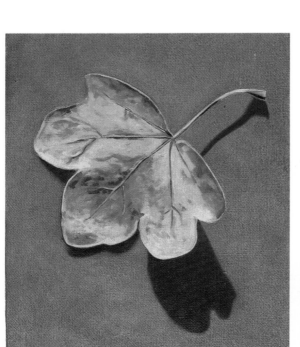

Producing harmony
This leaf study has first been painted in a range of tones of one colour, or "monochromatically", using Burnt Umber mixed with Titanium White for an opaque effect. When this is dry a glaze of Winsor Green has been applied over the surface of the leaf, with Cadmium Lemon for the highlights.

Deepening a colour
The tones on this garlic are given depth, and the image greater substance, using transparent glazes.

Touches of dark transparent Winsor Green are applied to the shadowy areas of the leaf.

Impasto

Oil paint can retain the crisp shape of a brushstroke, so it is well suited to the impasto technique. If you mix two colours together loosely and apply them with a brush, you can create a rich striated colour effect with a highly textured quality. Impasto can also be useful if you need to work quickly or on a large scale so that you can cover a surface with thick, expressive brushstrokes. Impasto is a technique that relies very much upon making every brushstroke achieve exactly the right feel and sense of immediacy, so many artists who work in this way often scrape off an area that doesn't work and make the impasted brushstroke again.

Impasted brushstrokes heighten the rich, buttery quality of oil paint.

Thick paint can pick up light shining on it so that it seems to sparkle.

Retaining the shape of a brushstroke

An impasto technique can echo the appearance of the image being painted. Here the rough texture of a shell is reflected in these chunky brushstrokes. Applied wet-in-wet, the thick strokes of paint intermingle slightly so that streaks of colour accentuate the textural effect of each brushtroke.

Thickly applied oil paint retains the marks or ridges left by a brush.

Lively brushstrokes

Painted largely with primary hues mixed with white, this image is built up with small touches of impasted high-key colour. No colour has been mixed with more than one other hue. Secondary blue-greens and oranges also predominate, vying with the yellows and reds. Touches of pure white have been added last for the highlights. Placed side by side, these separate brushstrokes create a lively patchwork of vibrant colour.

Loosely painted impasted brushstrokes break up the surface of a painting to create expression and vitality.

Rich impasted colours and brushstrokes dancing in all directions are held in check within the "arrow-head" composition of the two figures.

BRUSHWORK EFFECTS

Look for interesting textures and surfaces in familiar scenes

PICKING THE RIGHT BRUSH is part of the skill of effective brushwork and this choice takes practice. Soft hair brushes are most suitable for smooth effects and painting intricate work on a small scale. Hog hair or bristle brushes produce more "visible" brushstrokes, manipulating the oil paint into strong, vigorous shapes. Impasted strokes of thick colour made with a hog hair brush can also exploit the rich texture of oil paint and give life to a work. When you paint, the amount of expression that you give to each brushstroke will determine the character and vitality of the work. Try to keep the images big and bold, working economically with large, loose brushstrokes. Remember that if you practise blending, you need to actually disguise individual brushstrokes and fuse the joins between colours and tones in order to create fully modelled images.

1 ◀ Often the most familiar scene or subject matter can reveal interesting textures and surfaces. This café has both rough and smooth surfaces and a strong light that throws some areas into dusky shadows. Sketch the composition in with a large brush and then block in areas with colour and establish patterns using a small or a medium-sized bristle brush and paint thinned with turpentine.

2 ◀ The first layers of thin paint should dry quite quickly. Drag a medium-sized bristle brush, loaded with colour, over the dry surface to give a scumbled effect. The broken colour should give the surface greater texture and a deeper tone.

WIPING OFF

The great advantage of oil paint is that it takes a long time to dry, so if you need to get rid of an unwanted brushstroke or colour, use a piece of clean cloth to wipe off the mark carefully. Use one end of the cloth dipped in turpentine if you want to wipe the surface completely clean.

3 ▶ Overlay areas in shadow with darker tones. If you need to soften outlines or colours to give smooth gradations in tone or hue, wipe a clean finger over the paint so that the colours mingle gently.

4 ◄ The marble top of this table has a cool, polished appearance, so paint a layer of violet over areas in shadow and then complement the violet with yellow highlights. Once these underlayers are dry, apply a cool mixture of Titanium White with a touch of Cerulean Blue over the table top. Use a small clean sable brush to blend the paint to an even finish so that it looks like smooth marble. The underlayers of violet and yellow should show through faintly to suggest areas of light and shade.

5 ▶ Paint a thin transparent glaze of Alizarin Crimson over the floor area with a large synthetic wash brush to deepen the tone of the first hue. Mix the colour with a little oil painting medium first if you need to make it more malleable.

6 ▶ Paint thick impasted highlights on any bright objects with a small round bristle brush. Keep the paint as thick and as rich as possible so that the brushstrokes look bold and eye-catching.

7 ▲ Add definition to smooth objects by using a clean flat synthetic brush to blend the paint evenly and to create strong outlines. Paint the brushstrokes in the same direction so that the join between each stroke remains invisible.

The Café Scene

Different brushstrokes give a rich variety of textures in this study. The smooth marble table catches the eye, leading it to the centre of the scene. A transparent glaze on the floor creates a subtle, luminous quality, while impasted highlights stand out in relief. Scumbled walls at the back of the café create a hazy, distant feel.

A dry brush technique on these wooden chairs increases their grainy appearance.

Tea cups have been blended to look like smooth china.

Sharon Finmark

Materials

Size 10 flat synthetic brush

1in synthetic wash brush

Size 1 round hog hair brush

Size 5 long filbert hog hair brush

Size 8 short flat hog hair brush

GALLERY OF BRUSHWORK

THESE PAINTINGS GIVE a good indication of the range of brushwork effects that can be achieved with oil paint, from the smoothly blended "invisible" brushwork of Meredith Frampton to the boldly impasted strokes of Emil Nolde and the beautifully loose, expressive work of Manet. An artist's brushwork is much like handwriting – in revealing the intention and perhaps the personality of its author. Paint can be dabbed tentatively on to the canvas or stirred thickly and vigorously. A brushstroke can be fluent and deft, or clumsy and heavy. It can give movement and life to an area of the canvas, or hold an image or scene with controlled precision. The particular quality of brushwork also depends on the specific brush used.

Ben Levene RA, *Mixed Dried Flowers*, 1992, *130 x 111cm (51 x 43¾ in)*
This work subsumes a variety of different brushstrokes. Loose, scumbled brushmarks on the mirror convey a sense of distance, while objects in the foreground are painted in with careful, yet decisive small brushstrokes.

Roger Oakes,
First of Summer,
122 x 122 cm (48 x 48 in)
In this lively composition the brushwork is loose and strong, following first the diagonal line of the sea, and then becoming varied and more agitated around the bird's wings. Details are also freely painted.

Daisy designs on the girl's skirt, shown clearly in this detail, are built up of particularly relaxed brushstrokes.

White highlights are sketched on loosely with opaque white paint so that they create a simple, yet effective pattern.

Emil Nolde, *In the Lemon Garden,*
1933, *73 x 88 cm (28¾ x 35½ in)*
This painting carries off its mood of unabashed and tender romanticism because Nolde has painted it with such direct assurance and expression. Clear shapes of saturated colour have been applied with thick, heavy brushstrokes so that solid blocks of bright yellow, red, and orange glow against the loosely painted dark greens and purples in the background. The cool blue of the woman's face and arms have also been broken up by scumbling thicker, drier paint across the canvas. Such evocative brushstrokes give a feeling of joyfulness amidst the sultry perfumes of this secret arbour.

The delicate blending between individual brushstrokes gives a rounded poise to each element of the work and creates a mood of quiet stillness.

Meredith Frampton, *Portrait of a*
Young Woman, 1935, *108 x 25 cm (42½ x 9¾ in)*
This work is a good example of tones and colours that have been blended so perfectly that there is almost no evidence of visible brushwork. This is illusionistic painting at its most refined and it gives the figure and the objects the rather cool quality of smooth marble.

This detail demonstrates how the edge of an area of oil paint has been smoothed where it abuts with another colour so that there is no harsh edge linking the two.

Édouard Manet, *Au Bal, c.***1870-80,** *56 x 36 cm (22 x 14 in)*
This loosely worked study clearly shows the marks of each brushstroke as Manet worked rapidly to capture a profile. The sense of immediacy arises from a vivacity and economy in the brushwork, with a busy cluster of horizontal strokes describing the dress and more controlled strokes for the hair.

CHOOSING A SUPPORT

A SUPPORT IS THE SURFACE that you paint on and the type of material you choose is ultimately a personal choice. You can paint either on a rigid support such as a board or a panel, or a flexible support such as canvas, but within that choice there are a range of different surface textures to pick from that affect the way the paint behaves. Canvases and boards each have their own characteristic feel, and there is a big difference between the two. A hard rigid support enables you to prepare a roughly textured surface for painting that would be quite impractical on a stretched canvas, but the flexibility and texture of canvas makes it a far more responsive surface on which to paint.

Canvas boards
These combine the rigidity of board and the texture of canvas. Although available from artists' suppliers, they are easily made by gluing linen to a piece of hardboard and then priming the entire surface.

Blockboard

Plywood

Chipboard

Hardboard

Medium density fibreboard

Types of panel and canvas

Rigid supports provide a sounder and more permanent basis for painting. The advantage of using a board is that you can alter its surface texture by "priming" it roughly or smoothly (*see* p.37). Wooden panels covered with linen are particularly durable. The most common materials for panels nowadays are fabricated boards such as plywood, hardboard, and fibreboard, rather than the traditional mahogany, poplar, and oak. Hardboard is a good choice, particularly for smaller panels. A recent development is honeycomb aluminium, which provides a strong support.

A traditional flexible support is linen canvas, and the flax fibres from which linen is woven are long and strong. Cotton fibres are not so strong, but some excellent cotton canvases are available in heavier weights. You should use at least a ten ounce canvas cloth, and preferably a twelve ounce one. Weight is not so important when choosing a linen canvas. A new material, though not yet widely available, is the flexible, yet stable, polyester sailcloth.

Ready-primed canvas

Cotton duck 12oz

Coarse linen

Fine linen

Grained cotton

Cotton duck 15oz

Rough and smooth boards

A rough surface breaks up the smoothness of a brushstroke, giving it a pitted or textured appearance and producing a craggy, chunky version of an image (below). The board needs to be primed with loose brushstrokes to create this expressive effect, perhaps with sand in the primer to give a gravelly texture (see p.54). Use the back of a piece of hardboard if you prefer a regular texture. Bristle brushes also increase the degree of texture. On a smoothly primed board, soft hair brushes give more control modelling and blending forms and details. Alternatively, make sweeping brushstrokes that are unimpeded by any texture on the support so that you see each brushstroke with clarity (right).

The rough texture of these brushstrokes and the rugged appearance of the work is provided entirely by the nature of the ground.

This smooth ground shows up the texture of both thick and thin brushstrokes.

The energy of these brushstrokes retains a sense of freshness and immediacy.

Rough and smooth canvases

The texture of canvas can vary enormously, from the smooth, hard surface of wet-spun linen made from fine flax, to the rough texture of dry-spun coarse linen made from tow flax. Generally the finer the woven canvas, the smoother it will feel, and the more refined your painting will be. A smooth canvas enables you to work with great precision and detail with soft hair brushes, while a coarse canvas encourages a more vigorous approach with bristle brushes. Try various grades and types of surface to see what kind of canvas will best suit your style of painting.

The dry brush technique on this coarse, open-weave canvas makes the work seem part of the texture of the support. The harshness of the material echoes the knotty, rough quality of fishing nets, creating a continuity from the image of fishing boats to the surface quality of the painting.

The smooth quality of this fine weave canvas allows each small image to be painted clearly and delicately. Paint can be applied easily to this type of canvas and the flexibility of the cloth encourages a light, refined painting style.

35

PREPARING SUPPORTS & GROUNDS

Materials

Wooden stretcher pieces

Scissors

Staple gun

Wedges

Hammer

Linen canvas

CHOOSE A SUPPORT that suits your painting style. It can be rigid and stable, such as a wooden panel made of oak or poplar, or more commonly of hardboard or plywood; or it can be flexible, made of cotton, linen, or polyester canvas. The ground is what you put on the surface of the support in order to prepare it for painting. The surface is initially sized to seal it and prevent oil from the paint from being absorbed into the wood or canvas. A primer, either toned or white, can then be applied over the dried sizing.

Stretching a canvas

1 ◀ Start by slotting the four edges of the stretcher together. Tap a rubber hammer on each corner if the pieces become stuck.

2 ▶ Lay the stretcher over a large piece of canvas and then cut around it with scissors, leaving at least 8cm (3in) of canvas clear.

3 ▶ Stretch the linen canvas over the rigid wooden frame with thick staples and a staple gun, in rotation (*see* diagram, *right*). The order in which the staples are attached should ensure that the taut canvas has an even tension. Try to fold the canvas over the frame firmly rather than pulling hard; if you stretch it too tightly, it may begin to strain and distort in places.

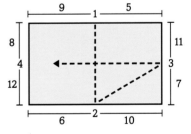

The canvas must be stapled in a specific order

4 ◀ Once the sides of the canvas have been attached securely to the frame, maintain an even tension at each corner of the support by stapling down the overlapping material. Neatly make two folds out of the canvas and then pull one fold over the other. Secure the folds to the frame with a staple.

5 ▲ Finally, tap four wedges into each corner of the frame with the hammer. These wedges help to tighten the frame a little more, making it as rigid and as taut as possible.

Sizing and priming a canvas

Materials

Dry rabbit skin glue

Plaster of paris

1 ▲ To size a canvas, heat 1 litre (2pt) of water in a double boiler (or a pot in a saucepan) with 30 grams (1oz) of dry rabbit skin glue. Paint the mix over the canvas with a general purpose 8cm (3in) brush.

2 ▲ When the sizing has dried completely, prime the canvas by adding gesso powder – plaster of paris – to the glue size until you get the consistency of double cream. Then cover the canvas with the white primer.

Sizing and priming a panel

1 ◀ Panels should also be sized, but add 70 grams (2½oz) of rabbit skin glue to the water.

2 ▲ When all the surfaces of the panel have been sized and are dry, prime them with gesso primer.

3 ◀ Once dry, sand the panel with very fine sandpaper to give it a smooth and even finish.

4 ▶ Finally, apply one more layer of glue size to the whole panel to seal the surfaces completely.

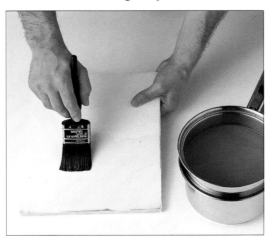

Double boiler

General purpose brush

Medium density fibreboard

Sandpaper

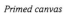

Primed canvas

Roughly primed board

Smoothly primed board

WAYS OF WORKING

MOST ARTISTS BEGIN TO DEVELOP their own techniques and individual style after a long period of experimentation and discovery. As a beginner, it makes sense to experiment as much as possible with many different approaches to painting so that you can build up a technical repertoire and discover ways of working that suit your own personality.

The basic art of painting

If you begin by painting small, simple objects, preferably with some sort of personal meaning, you will be able to concentrate on how you paint and not worry about extraneous details, or the initial difficulties of drawing. If you look at the work of past and present painters whose style you admire, you will see that in most cases it is largely a question of what is actually left out in the process of painting that makes their work so successful (*see* Galleries *throughout*). Simple domestic objects or toys make good subjects when you start to paint. They generally have a nice simplicity, which makes them appropriate subjects for drawing and painting. Start by painting what you see as straightforwardly as possible, and then concentrate on different ways of approaching the same subject. You may find it easier to begin working on a small scale in a rather careful style, drawing the outlines of the subject and pre-mixing a small range of tones, and then carefully filling the outlines in, stage by stage, with a soft hair or small bristle brush.

This is a good way of discovering the feel of the medium and learning how to control your brushes. After all, the basic art of painting is very much about matching what you can see, imagine, or even recall, with a particular mixture of colour applied in a certain way.

Developing style and technique

Painting familiar subjects will help you to build up the confidence to experiment with the objects you work with. Practise laying in the shadows on a flower with a range of tones, for instance, or blending separate colours with a dry brush to achieve the smooth, rounded finish of an egg. If you choose to paint a rough textural object, such as a piece of driftwood or a small rock, try a different technical approach and represent the crags and facets that characterize these objects with a range of different tones and loose, chunky brushstrokes.

Complex arrangements

Once you have looked at individual objects on their own, you may decide to paint a more complex arrangement that includes a number of objects. Here your approach to painting can be just the same, except that you will have to make decisions about how you organize your composition. Try to establish a sense of balance between the forms. This does not mean that what you see must be staid and solid, more that there should be a link or a thread running through the arrangement that binds it together.

You should also decide what kind of visual impact you want the composition to make. A composition that fills the frame will convey a sense of boldness and generosity – or you can create a feeling of separateness or isolation by painting gaps between the objects. This kind of experimentation with simple, accessible forms can be invaluable in experimenting with styles and approaches, giving you the confidence you need before deciding to tackle the more difficult subjects of portraits and landscapes.

Visual aids

It can be helpful to use photographs for visual reference when you work on a complicated subject such as a landscape, as you have the benefit of a three-dimensional scene or object already transcribed into a flat, two-dimensional image. Try to paint freely and not to copy the image exactly as it appears, as the painting can become cramped and look awkward. It is better to make a free transcription that leaves out all the unnecessary details and allows you to practise looking, for example, for cooler colours and lighter tones towards the horizon which help to increase the sense of aerial perspective.

Working with confidence

When you come to work freely with any subject in any situation, the kinds of simplifications that you have practised previously are all still entirely appropriate. When working from life, an artist needs to make a mental synthesis of the subject being painted, select the most interesting elements that will override the mass of extraneous detail, and allow the painting to develop as a succinct and self-contained world in its own right. In this way you will learn to discover a painting style that is most suited to you, and to adapt techniques to create new and unusual effects.

CREATING A COMPOSITION

COMPOSITION IS A TERM THAT DESCRIBES the organization of space in a picture – ordering shapes, forms, and colours in a way that is appropriate to the meaning of the image. When you are putting a composition together, look for balance and a sense of appropriateness, trusting your intuition. If you are working from life, look at the image through a viewfinder. Move it closer to and then further away from the image until you see the composition you want. If you are working from a photograph, try cropping areas of the image with small strips of paper.

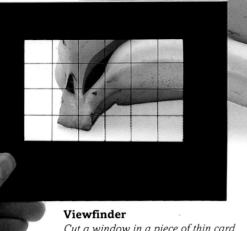

Viewfinder
Cut a window in a piece of thin card and use it to look for the best composition.

Looking for a composition
The most interesting composition is usually one that can give an image a fresh slant so that you perceive it in a new way. Arrange a still life composition on a table top, and then sketch it from as many different angles as you can think of. Try to be adventurous, closing right in on the still life or sketching just a few elements of the composition.

Visual impact
As you sketch, look for the way coloured objects react with each other to create a subtle harmony or a vibrant contrast. You may want to rearrange objects to achieve a better visual impact.

Transferring a sketch
Once you have selected the most interesting composition (right), the best way of transferring it to a canvas or a board is to use a grid system (see also below right). Place a grid over the original sketch and draw a similar grid on a larger scale on the support. Transfer details from each square on the sketch using charcoal (bottom), or drawing directly with a brush and a thin mix of paint (below). Pencil can be used very faintly, but it is generally not recommended as it can soil the colour of the paint. Some artists like to fill the outlines of shapes with light cross-hatching to determine areas of tone.

USING SLIDES

Slides can be used to transfer an image, whether it is a favourite scene, or a slide of the sketch itself. Hang a panel or a canvas on a wall, and shine the image on to it using a projector. You can determine very easily how large you want the image to be by moving the zoom lens on the projector. Then trace in the basic outlines of the composition with a piece of charcoal or a brush and a thin mix of paint. Polaroid pictures or photographs can also be useful for visual reference while you are painting, but you may like to crop the image first with small strips of paper to select a simplified or unusual composition.

If you draw directly
with a brush, use a thin mix of paint in a light or neutral colour so that it does not show through the painting.

Drawing grid
Draw a grid of squares on to a piece of tracing paper or acetate and then place it over the original sketch. This may seem like a laborious process of transferring an image, but it is a useful way of making sure the proportions of the composition remain intact.

Drawing grid

Doughy bread

Dusting off
If you draw with charcoal, use a large soft hair brush or a piece of doughy bread to dust the charcoal off and leave the residual image as a guide. Another option is to seal the charcoal with a fixative.

COMPOSITION

LOOKING AT A LANDSCAPE or an interior, it can be difficult to know quite where to establish the broad areas of a composition for painting. It can sometimes be helpful to think of the eye like a camera lens, zooming in on a scene to focus on just one element, or pulling back to encompass a wide viewpoint and include more visual information. You will also need to decide what the boundaries of your composition will be. An image can be placed partially within the frame, so that the picture seems part of a much larger scene, or placed centrally so that every aspect of the scene is contained within the frame. Unusual angles and perspectives can create added interest.

Make several sketches to discover the most interesting composition

1 ▶ Select the most suitable composition and transfer the sketch on to the canvas with the aid of a drawing grid. This grid system should help you retain the correct proportions of the sketch as you draw the composition out on the canvas.

2 ▶ Block in the main elements of the composition with areas of flat colour, thinned with turpentine. As this interior scene has sharp distinctions of lights and darks, try to establish these areas as soon as possible so that they stay clearly defined.

3 ▲ Build up the tones and shadows on each individual object to heighten the colour and establish a sense of light. The thick stroke of dark colour on this jug gives it more of a three-dimensional form.

4 ◀ Mix two separate colours to build up the lights and darks on this chair. One mix of Viridian, Cadmium Yellow, Raw Sienna, and Yellow Ochre, painted on with a medium-sized bristle brush, captures the light hitting the back of the chair. A touch of Ultramarine Blue with the Viridian gives dark shadows.

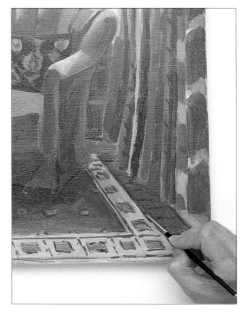

6 ◀ The carpet and curtains in this painting play an important part in establishing a strong sense of perspective; both carpet and curtains recede at a sharp angle, so patterns or markings at the edge of the carpet should be painted proportionally smaller. Paint such details with a fine sable or synthetic brush to keep the effects soft.

5 ▲ Once an area has been built up with thin paint, overlay it with more saturated mixes of bright colour to give the effect of strong light. When you describe the intensity of such bright light, keep the contrast between each colour as sharp and as clean as possible. Deepen dark areas to make this contrast more dramatic.

7 ◀ The landscape visible through the large windows should be painted in much paler colours to create a sense of distance and aerial perspective (*see right*). Dab touches of colour lightly over the canvas with a medium-sized bristle brush. A dark glaze over the window frame helps it retain its rich colour and contrast with the pale light beyond.

AERIAL PERSPECTIVE

Aerial perspective is a term that describes the effect of atmospheric conditions on our perception of the tone and colour of distant objects. As objects recede towards the horizon they appear to become bluer and lighter in tone. Artists generally work from light tones at the back of the composition to the darker tones at the front.

Jude's Sitting Room
This painting really describes a frame within a frame. The perspective created by the curtains and carpet lead the eye up into the central area of the painting, which has every object at an angle to increase the degree of interest in the composition.

A good variation of tone and colour describes objects well and keeps the composition lively.

Dark shadows contrast with strong areas of light and pale colour through the windows.

Darker, stronger colours in the foreground push the bottom of the painting forward to catch the eye and increase the perspective of the painting.

Jane Gifford

Materials

Size 4 round sable brush

Size 1 round hog hair brush

Size 8 round synthetic brush

Size 4 long flat hog hair brush

Well-balanced colours help to create a strong closed composition.

GALLERY OF COMPOSITION

COMPOSITION IS ALL ABOUT establishing an appropriate relationship between various elements of your painting, such as form, tone, and colour, so that together they generate the meaning you want a painting to convey. When you establish the basic structure of a composition, ask yourself whether it communicates what you want to say about your subject, or whether changing the size, position, or structure of a particular feature will make your work clearer. The variety of composition in these paintings each creates a different impact. A low viewpoint in one painting can cause isolated objects to appear dramatically bold and create a strong psychological effect, while a high viewpoint in another work allows individual components to become part of a broader scene that stretches away before the viewer in a pleasing, leisurely way.

Simon Ripley, *On the Edge,* *43 x 36 cm (17 x 14 in)*
Ripley's unusual composition places a vase on the far end of a table as if it is spinning off the edge. Large areas of orange-red complement the small active cool blue of the vase in this strange and evocative work.

Oskar Kokoschka,
Broad View of the Thames,
1926, *89 x 130 cm (35 x 51 in)*
Kokoschka's painting is an excellent example of the way an artist can manipulate space within a composition in order to show more of the panorama than is possible with a conventional linear perspective. Here Kokoschka has utilised a form of curvilinear perspective, pushing the painting into an all-embracing circular composition. The artist's high viewpoint also allows more of the river and ground to be included in his panoramic sweep.

Bill Jacklin RA, *The Rink III*,
1991, *198 x 183 cm (78 x 72 in)*
This image of moving ice skaters creates a very effective open
composition, a term which implies a continuation beyond the
bounds of the canvas. There is a wonderful sense of swaying
movement in the painting, brought about by the angle of the
figures in the middle-ground and foreground and their long
shadows that sweep down on a diagonal, impelling the eye
down and around through the moving bodies. There is also
a kind of icy breathiness about the colour scheme of the work
that perfectly recalls the physical atmosphere of the scene.

Carel Weight RA, *The*
***Frustrated Tiger*, 1992,**
181 x 151 cm (71¼ x 59½ in)
The two pairs of figures in
this unusual composition
create a strange symmetry,
with unexplained shapes
and strange shadows
linking them all together.
The turbulent sunset,
together with the distant
childlike image of the tiger,
combine to create a quite
extraordinary atmosphere.

Sir Robin Philipson RA,
***Poppies, c.*1985,**
76 x 102 cm (30 x 40 in)
This study of poppies is
a fine example of a closed
composition, in which
everything is contained
within the frame. The vase
and flowers fill the space
generously without going
beyond it. The adjacent
harmony of the powerfully
warm hues intensifies this
small, closed world.

PAINTING ON A WHITE GROUND

A WHITE GROUND PROVIDES a perfect surface for reflecting the purity of a colour painted over it. A transparent colour that looks dark in a tube appears as a brilliant saturated hue when it is painted thinly over a white surface. Semi-opaque and even opaque colours are also given a particular clarity on a white ground, especially since there is often a variation in thickness between individual brushstrokes. Generally, more painting is required on a white ground in order to cover the white surface, while a coloured or toned ground provides a useful unifying matrix between the brushstrokes of different colour.

Influencing the look of a colour
These examples of Permanent Rose demonstrate how easily the appearance of a colour changes. The top squares, painted first thickly, and then thinly on a white surface, retain their brilliance and purity, while the coloured ground beneath subdues the luminosity of the transparent paint.

Make a sketch on white paper to plan the colour scheme

SINCE WHITE REPRESENTS the brightest highlight a painter can create, most of the white ground in this exercise has been covered to achieve a more accurate representation of tones. As you paint over the white ground, bear in mind that the colours you paint will initially look much darker on the dazzling white surface than they will when you have finished the painting and covered up most of the white ground.

1 ◀ A white ground suits this subject matter perfectly, as it can illuminate the colours painted over it to give a sensation of strong summer light. Sketch the landscape with thinned paint and a small round bristle brush, and then block in main areas of colour with a clean brush.

2 ◀ This work relies on strong colour to make its impact, so use pure complementary colours to achieve the maximum effect. Pick out areas of the foreground with warm colours such as orange, yellow, and red, and then complement them with cooler colours in the distance such as blue, violet, and green. Cover as much of the white surface as possible with the thin mixes of colour.

3 ◀ Use a cold, clean blue, such as Cerulean Blue, for the sky. To avoid painting a heavy, flat area of colour, lighten some Ultramarine Blue with touches of white and use it to break up the large expanse of sky with a long filbert bristle brush. Keep this paint dry and thick so that you can create a scumbled effect over the first layer of paint. This should give the sky a richer texture and a deeper tone.

4 ▶ Once you have covered all the white ground, you may find that some areas of colour still look quite weak, so refine and strengthen the look of objects with mixes of bright, saturated colour. Use a versatile green, such as Winsor Green, to increase the range of tones and emphasize the particular shape of each tree. Use a small round bristle brush for any intricate details. If the particular area you are working on is still wet with paint, maintain a steady hand by using a mahl stick (*see* p.15).

5 ▲ Apply a pale mix of Cerulean Blue, lightened with white and painted in with a fine sable brush, to provide an effective contrast with the warm orange rooftops. The coolness of the mix also increases the sense of aerial perspective in the painting.

6 ◀ Add strokes of hot colour, such as pure Cadmium Red, to enliven the foreground area and contrast with the banks of green trees beyond. Use a dry brush technique and plenty of saturated paint to give both texture and brilliance to the final look of the painting.

A dry brush technique breaks up large areas of colour, but the touches of white ground that show through also increase the brilliance of this blue paint.

Materials

Size 2 round sable brush

Size 1 round hog hair brush

Size 5 long filbert hog hair brush

Provence Landscape
A white ground enables saturated colours to show their freshness and brilliance in this painting. The hot summer atmosphere is heightened by several complementary colours that enhance one another to look even brighter. Energetic brushstrokes and interesting texture give the scene movement and vitality.

Warm colours painted in the foreground are complemented by cool background colours that create aerial perspective.

Paula Velarde

PAINTING ON A TONED GROUND

THE GREAT ADVANTAGE of working on a toned or coloured ground is the economy it can bring to your painting technique. Paint darker tones in transparent colours, which allow the ground colour to show through, and lighter tones in opaque colours, which obliterate it. The mid-tones are provided by the colour of the ground itself, so that you soon have a work with a very finished appearance. It would take much longer to reach the same point working on a white ground. The Yellow Ochre mid-toned ground used in the exercise below provides a warm underlying tone for the work and acts as a unifying element in the painting.

PREPARING A TONED GROUND

There are two ways of colouring a ground – either by laying a thin transparent veil of colour over the white priming, which is known as an imprimatura – or by laying an opaque layer of colour over the primer. Allow plenty of time for the colour to dry before painting.

1 *A toned ground can be any colour, but warm red ochres and browns can give more richness to a work. A thin transparent wash of imprimatura can be made by mixing Burnt Umber and Yellow Ochre, and adding white spirit to reduce the paint mixture to a thin consistency. Apply the imprimatura freely and evenly over the support, in this case a panel, with a large bristle brush.*

2 *Let the solvent in the mixture evaporate for a few minutes and then rub the surface with a cloth to take away the excess paint. This means that the white priming has a stain of transparent colour rather than a coat of paint. The main advantage of using an imprimatura rather than a toned ground is that the film of colour allows the white of the original priming to retain its reflective quality on the colours painted over it.*

The opaqueness of a coloured ground ensures a complete uniformity of tone over the surface of the support. A coloured ground can also be laid by mixing colour in with the primer itself before it is applied.

Toning a primed canvas
This canvas support has already been primed with white primer, and a coloured ground made of Burnt Umber, Yellow Ochre, and Titanium White is laid over the top with a large wash brush. A coloured ground will take longer to dry than an imprimatura, so ensure that it is completely dry before you begin to paint. Most coloured grounds will take a few days to dry completely.

1 ◀ Sketch in the composition with a medium-sized bristle brush and a thin mix of Burnt Umber. The ground has been prepared with a mix of Yellow Ochre, Gold Ochre, and Titanium White.

2 ▶ Break up and enliven areas of the coloured ground using a medium-sized bristle brush and a slightly thicker mixture of Yellow Ochre with a touch of Titanium White and Cadmium Red.

3 ▲ Once you have blocked in all the shapes and dark areas of shadow with thin colour, start to build up the highlights on each figure using a thick, dry mix of Titanium White, Alizarin Crimson, and Yellow Ochre and a medium-sized filbert bristle brush.

Size 6
short filbert hog hair brush

Size 7
long filbert hog hair brush

Size 5
long flat hog hair brush

Size 1 round hog hair brush

Size 1 round sable brush

4 ▲ Use a small brush, such as a size 1 round hog hair, to add finer details to the background and create aerial perspective. These details should be painted over dry layers to avoid mixing paint.

5 ◄ Build more texture into the middle ground by scumbling a mix of Raw Umber with a small flat bristle brush.

6 ◄ Increase the sense of light falling across the scene with layers of light colour over the initial washes. Using a cool mixture of Titanium White, Yellow Ochre, and a touch of Viridian, paint light gestural strokes over shadowed areas with a large filbert bristle brush. For warm areas add a little Alizarin Crimson instead of the Viridian.

7 ◄ Paint distant figures and objects with a cool brown such as Raw Umber using a fine brush, such as a size 1 sable round. When these details have dried, use even paler colour in the background to increase the sense of aerial perspective and hazy light.

Indian Street Dwellers

The look of this painting is clearly affected by the warm colour of the toned ground, influencing the appearance of every hue in the composition. The finished look the ground gives allows the brushstrokes to be made quite sparingly using paint thinned with turpentine to establish the scene, and thicker highlights to finish.

Shanti Thomas

The coloured ground provides an effective base for subtle juxtapositions of warm and cool colour to be laid on top of it.

Dark tones have been painted with thinner transparent colours, while the lighter tones and highlights have been created with thick opaque colour.

Coloured grounds give a more finished effect, allowing for a much looser and relaxed style of painting.

The mid-toned ground links separate areas of colour and gives an overall warmth to the painting.

GALLERY OF WHITE & TONED GROUNDS

THE PAINTINGS SHOWN HERE demonstrate how important the colour of any ground is, from the bright clarity of colour that can be produced on a white ground to the economy of painting on a subtle mid-toned ground. A toned ground not only affects the appearance of a colour painted immediately on top of it, but also any successive layers of transparent and opaque paint.

Mick Rooney RA, *Wedding Day Yalalag*, 1991, *91 x 71 cm (36 x 28 in)*
The principle of opaque highlights and transparent shadows on a dark ground is well illustrated in this painting of a village wedding. Opaque colours are worked stiffly in a scumbled dry brush technique that allows the dark ground colour to show through in half tone effects.

Donald Hamilton Fraser RA, *Grand Canal, Venice,* 1992, *76 x 58 cm (30 x 23 in)*
This is an excellent example of a painting made directly in an economical style on a white ground. The paint, applied thinly, allows the white ground to illuminate colours and give clarity and a sparkle to the quality of light in the painting. Areas of high contrast add a crisp brightness to the scene.

This detail shows how clean and strong the colours look on a white ground.

The glimpses of white ground still visible help to intensify the appearance of each colour.

Pablo Picasso, *Head of a Sailor,* 1906-7, *40 x 42 cm (15¾ x 16½ in)*
The pastel-like quality of this work is due mainly to the fact that opaque white has been painted on to a dark ground and tinted with colour. The coloured ground shows through the brushstrokes, providing a strong backcloth to a subtle work. The effect of overlaying such a darkly-coloured background with an opaque dry brush technique pushes the simply styled image forwards so that we feel even closer to the absorbed character.

In this detail the dark ground enhances simple blocks of colour and the almost diagrammatical style of painting.

Thickly painted highlights over the dark ground make the work look more dramatic.

Paul Lewin, *Cornish Cliffs,* *44 x 51 cm (17½ x 20 in)*
The brown mid-toned ground of this work has allowed for economy when painting and provides a warm unifying background colour to link the individual brushstrokes. The artist has employed thin transparent darks for the shadows and thicker opaque colours for the lighter tones, reserving the lightest tones and thickest paint for the breaking waves.

Jane Gifford, *Calcutta Bus Trip,* *91 x 91 cm (36 x 36 in)*
This painting buzzes with warmth and humanity. It conveys the bustle and excitement of a busy Indian street in a series of relatively flat planes of bright saturated colours. Interlocking patterned shapes retain their clarity of colour, having been painted directly on to the white ground.

51

ALLA PRIMA PAINTING

Establish a composition

ALSO KNOWN AS direct painting, alla prima work is usually completed in one sitting while the paint remains wet on the support. Such paintings have an expressive immediacy and freshness. It is important to bear in mind that once a colour has been laid on, it will affect any colour that is subsequently painted on top of it while it is still wet, so if you sketch in the broad areas of the subject first, do so with thin paint. You need a clear idea of where colours will be placed, or the painting will become muddy.

Sketching from life
Conditions constantly change when you paint from life; a landscape can alter dramatically if the sun goes behind a cloud, and people can move all too easily. Make plenty of preparatory sketches to explore your subject and collect handy reference material.

The feline characteristics of this cat have been captured with simple lines and a hint of colour.

These economical studies are full of expression and interesting ideas.

1 ▲ Cats can move away instantly, so use a small support to enable you to work over the canvas as fast as possible. Outline the shape of the cat using a small brush, such as a size 1 round hog hair, and Ivory Black paint thinned with plenty of turpentine. Work quickly, making a line sketch to establish the position of the cat. Look for its essential features, keeping each brushstroke as loose and as expressive as possible. If you make a mistake, use the end of a cloth dipped in turpentine to wipe away the mark.

2 ◀ Plot the relationship of the cat to the cushion and armchair so that if the cat suddenly moves, the scale of the painting has already been planned. Then return to the cat and develop it as much as possible. Look for the way the light affects its distinguishing features, and which direction its fur grows. Describe the shape of the cat with a mixture of Ivory Black and Cerulean Blue, together with a little Titanium White. Flick the brush lightly to give the impression of fur.

3 ▲ Use an orange mixed from Cadmium Yellow Deep, Cadmium Orange, and Titanium White to build up areas of the sketched cushion with light colour. Avoid mixing in white paint when you fill in the darker areas of the cushion. Keep brushstrokes loose and full of expression to retain a sense of freshness.

4 ◀ Use a larger bristle brush to block in the colour of the armchair and the wall behind. The broken colour of the background must be cool and subdued so that it does not detract from the main subject. Take time to clean your brushes thoroughly before you apply each new colour – working at this speed, you should guard against mistakes such as muddying your colours. Take the paint up to the edge of each separate area of colour without overpainting it.

Materials

Size 2 round sable brush

Size 1 round hog hair brush

Size 5 long filbert hog hair brush

5 ▶ Any gaps showing through in the canvas between broad areas of colour can be covered up using a small bristle brush. Here the gaps can be covered by emphasizing the cat's wispy fur. Stroke touches of pure Cerulean Blue lightly over the first colours to give interesting texture and definition to the cat.

6 ▶ Take a fine brush, such as a size 2 round sable, to deepen the shadows on the cat. Using a sable brush should allow you to apply fresh colour over a layer of wet paint if you want to avoid mixing the two. Mix a small amount of Cerulean Blue paint with the Ivory Black to keep the shadows cool.

7 ▶ Work up the remaining areas of the composition once you are satisfied with the look of the cat. Deepen the folds and shadows of the cushion with pure Cadmium Orange. Use simple tonal variations of Yellow Ochre and Burnt Sienna to mould the wooden armchair.

Cat on an Orange Cushion

This work has been planned in advance so that colours can be placed exactly without becoming muddy. The progress of the work has been geared around a subject that could move at any moment, but without compromising the characteristic sense of immediacy associated with this style.

A strong composition is important if you are working quickly from life.

Colours are kept clean and pure, with simple variations in tone.

Sue Sareen

WORKING WITH A PAINTING KNIFE

IF YOU ARE UNUSED to working with a painting knife, the first thing that will strike you is how different the paint feels using a knife in comparison with a brush. Working with a painting knife requires some delicacy, as it spreads the paint like butter on to bread; the flat surface of the painting knife seems to slice easily through the paint as you lay it on to the canvas. Whereas a paint brush tends to come down on to the canvas vertically, the painting knife can be applied horizontally, parallel to the surface of the painting. Painting knife studies are often made wet-in-wet, generally using more opaque colours.

Textured surfaces

A painting knife produces a variety of interesting textural effects simply by being held in different ways. If you want to increase the degree of texture on the surface of your support, mix some dry sand into the primer when you prepare the board. This builds up the surface of the support into a relief, pushing the painting into three dimensions.

Using a painting knife

A painting knife needs to be used with confidence and without hesitation, so it is worth practising first. Use a knife both for building up final highlights in thick impasto and for a textured, lively painting. Painting knives are not the same as palette knives, which are only intended for mixing paint and cleaning palettes; painting knives have a crank in the handle so that they can be held in several different ways to manipulate the creamy paint into expressive shapes (*see below*). Many artists use their finger on the springy blade, pushing it down deliberately to control the way the paint is applied. Since paint is usually applied very thickly with a painting knife it is sensible to work on a rigid support.

Horizontal strokes of thick, creamy paint from a loaded painting knife.

Use the length of the blade to smear paint over a surface.

Bold strokes

Grip the handle firmly, as you would a trowel, and paint decisive, vigorous strokes of colour across the surface of the support.

Wrap your fingers firmly around the wooden handle.

Small dabs of colour are useful for details.

Press gently into the paint with a finger on the back of the blade.

Light effects

For a lighter control of the painting knife, place your index finger on the springy part of the blade so that just the tip presses down into the paint.

Clean lines

A more common way of holding the knife is to place your index finger on the end of the wooden handle and push the metal shaft into the paint. This produces a firm imprint of the blade in the paint and is useful for making ridged lines of colour.

Use this technique to build up a regular pattern of texture.

A firm but even grip gives good control.

1 ◀ This portrait is built up on a small primed panel so that the paint can be scraped easily to give a more textural study. Make a quick sketch first with thinned paint if you need to work out correct proportions. Then smooth paint over the main areas of the portrait with light strokes.

2 ◀ When you have applied several different tones to the face and hair, use the edge of the painting knife, or a piece of card with serrated edges, to emphasize the direction the hair grows in. These create highlights on the hair and help to break up heavy layers of paint.

3 ▶ Smooth a clean finger gently over any area where you need to blend the paint; a painting knife is effective for crisp lines of colour, but it may be difficult to achieve the same degree of subtle blending that can be had with a brush or a finger.

Materials

Diamond-shaped painting knife

Serrated edge

Paint brush handle

4 ◀ Use the end of the painting knife, or the tip of a brush handle, if you want to make small dots of colour and build up the texture of the painting. Dip the brush handle in paint and use it to suggest the pattern of this cardigan.

Ridges of colour made with a painting knife catch the light to give the painting a brighter quality.

Paint is both smeared over the support and laid on with strokes of thick, impasted colour.

The texture of the paint gives the work an almost three-dimensional look.

Textural portrait
A variety of expressive textural marks give this portrait life. A painting knife is used to apply the paint quickly and produce crisp strokes of colour to establish the main features of the face. Additional techniques, such as lines and highlights made with a serrated edge and dabs of paint made with a brush handle, add to the textural surface. The painting knife has been used finally to apply thick impasted highlights.

Christian Furr

55

GALLERY OF ALLA PRIMA PAINTINGS

OIL PAINT IS SUCH a well-bodied and viscous material that it may be used in a variety of rich textural effects and brushstrokes. Painting from life can encourage this sense of freedom and expression when you work with oil paint, as it relies on a freshness and immediacy. Brushstrokes and marks appear more tangible if they have been painted wet-in-wet, or wiped off and reapplied, and the paintings shown here are examples of the wide-ranging results and instant appeal that can be achieved by incorporating different techniques and textural effects.

Vincent van Gogh, *The Hospital Garden at St Rémy,* **1889,** *63 x 48 cm (25 x 18 in)*
It would be difficult to make a more immediate statement in paint than this work by Van Gogh. Strong, stubby brushstrokes follow the forms of the painted objects, and the ground appears to move like a sea. The texture and rhythm of the brushstrokes across the surface of the painting give the scene an intense energy.

This detail shows particles of sand, blown by the wind, still embedded in the paintwork. The fluent brushwork seems to echo this tugging wind.

Claude Monet, *The Beach at Trouville,* **1870,** *38 x 46 cm (14¾ x 18 in)*
This study was painted rapidly on the beach at Trouville. Built over a warm pale grey ground, the work is striking in its immediacy and in the fluent brushwork. There is also much of the wet-in-wet work so characteristic of Monet, with fresh colours laid into one another.*

Ken Howard RA, *Blue and Gold Kimono,* 1991, *102 x 122 cm (40 x 48 in)*
The freshness of the brushwork in this scene gives a lively quality, although there is control in the painting style. The screen, for example, is carefully painted to give a loose, free impression. Broad planes of light and dark allow the artist to incorporate detail without overloading the composition. It is important to stress this idea of control in what comes across as a very spontaneous work.

The subtle pattern on this kimono is echoed in other areas of the painting.

This detail shows both the vigour and the control in the individual brushstrokes that create the pattern on the kimono.

Julian Schnabel, *The Geography Lesson,* **1980,** *224 x 214 cm (88 x 84 in)*
The buttery texture of oil on velvet in this work is heightened by impasted strokes of vivid colour. The subject matter is perfectly matched by the painting style.

Bernard Dunstan RA, *Piazza del Duomo, Orvieto,* **c.1991,** *37 x 40 cm (14½ x 15¾ in)*
This painting has an assurance of touch and economy, giving a relaxed quality and a real sense of space and light.

PAINTING IN LAYERS

IF YOU ARE NOT USED to building up a painting in layers, you should keep two things in mind. Firstly, always wait until a paint layer is completely dry before overpainting it with another colour, and secondly, add a drop or two more of your oil painting medium to your paint mixtures as you work up through the layers of colour. This ensures that each layer is slightly more flexible than the one below, and

is known as the "fat-over-lean" rule. Although there are many ways of painting in layers, one method is to sketch an image in diluted colour and then paint in the broad areas of tone with a transparent or monochromatic technique. When this is dry, colour can be added and paler tones worked in. Once these layers are dry, final applications of transparent glazes and opaque highlights can be added.

APPLYING A GLAZE

Transparent oil glazes should not simply be brushed on and left; they usually need to be manipulated with a brush on the support to give a uniformity of tone, even out the degree of colour saturation, or reduce a thick glaze to a light stain. A blending brush, or a clean shaving brush, is good for dabbing and smoothing the glaze. When you mix a glaze, add a glazing or painting medium to the paint to make it more malleable. Once you have painted on the glaze, wait for a few moments so that some of the solvent in the painting medium can evaporate. Then use the shaving brush to manipulate the glaze and smooth away visible brushmarks. If you only need glaze a small area, use a small round or flat soft hair brush instead.

1 An underpainting in one colour can be useful as it allows you to concentrate on form and tone first, rather than colour.

2 Once the underpainting is dry, apply colour over the different tones with a large bristle brush.

3 Smooth the glaze over the surface with a large, flat round brush, such as a shaving brush.

Building up layers of colour

A still life is a good subject to choose if you want to practise painting in layers, as you can leave the composition set up for as long as you need to wait for individual layers of paint to dry. This study is built up over a coloured ground to give the layers of colour a subtle accent. A monochromatic underpainting helps to establish areas of light and dark before any colours are applied. Mix each glaze you use with a little oil painting medium.

1 ◀ Sketch the composition in with a thin mix of Burnt Umber and then use a small round bristle brush and a range of grey tones to build up a tonal picture of each object in this still life.

2 ▲ When the underpainting has dried, mix individual glazes of colour and apply them with a large, flat synthetic wash brush. If you prefer, use a new brush for every glaze so that you can retain the purity of each colour.

3 ▶ When the first glazes are dry, mix a darker glaze of Permanent Red for the red stripes on the rug, adding a little more painting medium to increase the amount of oil in the next layer. Apply the deep transparent colour with a medium-sized bristle brush, and as these areas of red are quite small, use a sable brush to work the glaze to a smooth finish.

4 ◀ Add thin layers of strong colour to each object using a medium-sized brush, such as a size 6 long filbert hog hair. Dab the glaze gently with a round sable brush to manipulate the glaze and smooth away any uneven areas of paint. If paint builds up on the brush, wipe it off on a piece of absorbent tissue, or if you paint over any highlights, use the cloth to wipe away the unwanted paint.

5 ▲ Add a final glaze to the back wall with a large bristle brush to give a cooler, more shadowy effect. Use a clean, dry shaving brush to work the glaze in with short strokes.

Studio still life
This painting has been built up with layers of thin colour. The coloured ground provides a warm base for transparent glazes that are applied only after previous layers are thoroughly dry. Glazes over large areas are smoothed into a uniform tone with a shaving brush.

The tones on each object have been achieved with an underpainting.

Separate layers of transparent colour together give a rich, luminous effect.

The large area of the back wall is glazed with cool colour so that it appears to recede behind the still life.

Ian McCaughrean

Materials

Size 1 round hog hair brush

Size 6 short filbert hog hair brush

Size 6 long flat hog hair brush

1¼ in synthetic wash brush

Shaving brush

PAINTING IN STAGES

Preparatory sketch from life

THERE IS OFTEN an overlap of two or more techniques in any work. Although some paintings appear to have been painted directly from life, they may also have been built up with careful final stages to heighten the tone and effect of colours, or increase the element of detail. The work below has all the hallmarks of a painting from life, although in fact it has been built up in a series of carefully planned stages. In this kind of transitional painting, it is usual to begin by blocking in major areas of tone and colour, and then working into these with deeper glazes and more detail as the painting develops. The most important aspect of this process is that you add a new layer of paint only after the last layer is dry. A white ground retains the power and clarity of every colour.

1 ▷ Make a light sketch of the composition in charcoal, working out the position of trees and plants. If the lines look too harsh, try brushing off the excess charcoal with a soft hair brush or a piece of doughy bread (*see* pp.40-41). Excess charcoal can muddy the paint if it is left lying on the surface of the canvas, so another way to protect the paint is to spray a surface coating of fixative over the charcoal outlines.

2 ▷ Block in the main areas of the painting with thin areas of pure bright colour using a large or medium-sized bristle brush. Leave these first layers to dry before adding new paint.

3 ▲ Once the first layers of thin paint are dry, deepen separate areas of colour. Use a large synthetic wash brush to lay a thin, transparent glaze of Permanent Rose over the foreground area to deepen its tone. Mix a little oil painting medium into the Permanent Rose so that it can be manipulated more easily on the canvas. Use a clean, dry soft hair brush to brush the glaze into a uniform consistency over the canvas.

4 ◁ Use a long filbert bristle brush to paint in branches and leaves. Use cool colours for areas in shadow and a transparent mix of Winsor Green for brighter details to create a sense of distance and capture the airy spaciousness of this conservatory.

5 ◄ Once the layers of paint are dry again, start adding in details of the foliage. This is time-consuming work, as the trees and leaves should be painted individually to create movement and depth in the painting. Emphasize bark on the tree trunks by painting cool blue shadows using a small synthetic or sable brush.

6 ▶ The ironwork across the roof and the path down the centre hold the composition together, so paint them with strong clean colours to create visual impact. Use a small flat brush to paint the gratings on the path, and a small round synthetic brush to heighten the smooth metallic look of the ironwork beyond.

7 ▶ Finally, create a feeling of space by painting in small leaves with dabs of pale cool blue paint over the iron arch, which should help to push it further into the background. Darken areas in shadow if you need to increase the contrast of tones and colours that heighten the feeling of bright light in the painting.

The Palm House

The glasshouse atmosphere in this painting has been created using a white ground to keep the colours strong and retain a sense of immediacy. However, the paint has been built up in stages to increase the detailed look of the foliage and deepen the tone of transparent colours.

A white priming keeps colours strong and bright.

Touches of white paint give the impression of strong light shining through the roof.

Thick strokes of impasted colour have been painted last to give texture and definition.

Thin glazes of transparent colour deepen the tone of the foreground.

Ian McCaughrean

Materials

Charcoal

Size 8 long flat synthetic brush

Size 6 round sable brush

Size 6 long filbert hog hair brush

1½ in mixed fibre wash brush

GALLERY OF PAINTING IN LAYERS

PAINTING IN LAYERS has been integral to the art of painting for hundreds of years, and some systematic methods have evolved. The key to this technique is that each layer of paint is completely dry before more paint is applied. There are variations on this theme, ranging from refining a simple painting with highlights and shadows, to a more complex interweaving of transparent and opaque layers of paint to create sophisticated effects. Artists evolve their own methods of working, and the images shown here represent a variety of approaches.

Giovanni Moroni,
Portrait of a Widower with His Two Children, c.1565,
98 x 126 cm (38½ x 49½ in)
This painting has been layered in stages over a warm ground, and the depth of tone – so relevant to the meaning of the work – has been built up with transparent glazes. Bright pale tones are stacked up in opaque colour to provide contrast with the background. A dramatic poignancy arises from the juxtaposition of pure, primary colours on the children's skirts with the widower's dark costume and background.

Shanti Thomas,
Fruit Stall, 66 x 76 cm (26 x 30 in)
This is an example of a work that gives a strong, direct, and immediate impression, but was in fact built up in stages. The painting relies on overlaid touches of transparent, semi-opaque, and opaque paints in a patchwork of colour to create contrasted areas of tone and rich surface effects.

Ray Smith,
Dr McDonald,
91 x 69 cm (36 x 27 in)
Painted on a dark toned background, the attention of this work focuses sharply on the bright wrinkled face of an old man. Dark areas have been worked up with transparent glazes and highlights with opaque colour.

El Greco, *Vision of St John,* 1610-14
222 x 194 cm (87½ x 76¼ in)
El Greco may have modelled his drapery while the transparent glazes were still wet, reversing established practices and proving that there are no hard and fast rules in painting.

Sue Sareen,
Young Girl With a Cat, 91 x 71 cm (36 x 28 in)
This painting of the artist's daughter was built up indirectly in a few simple stages. The composition was both painted from life, and worked on from four separate photographs. The image was first drawn in charcoal and then sketched on top in Burnt Umber. Colours were then blocked in thinly and left to dry. The painting was finished two weeks later when the colours were built up in a more solid application.

A large area of Cadmium Red paint on the open door is echoed in other areas of the painting. This detail shows light strokes of Cadmium Red illuminating the girl's hair.

Touches of Cerulean Blue provide cool notes throughout the painting and offset the large areas of red.

63

EXPERIMENTAL TECHNIQUES

ARTISTS HAVE ALWAYS EXPERIMENTED with different ways of working with oil paint. One traditional technique is sgraffito, in which one colour is laid over another layer of dry colour and then scratched through with a sharp instrument so that the colour beneath is revealed as an image or pattern. Another technique is to paint or splash thick colours on to a canvas or board, lay a sheet of thin hard paper or plastic over the top, lift some of the paint off, and use the remaining image for special textural or surreal effects. Nowadays there are also new materials developed by manufacturers. A relatively recent product is the oil stick, which is basically oil paint in stick form. This allows you to draw with the oil paint as though it were a pastel or a piece of charcoal. It has a smooth, creamy feel and it is possible to work into a wet colour and still retain the colour of the stroke you are making.

Sgraffito

Sgraffito is an old method of drawing into a layer of wet paint to produce a line drawing of an image or a detail. When you scratch through the layer of wet paint you should reveal a new colour underneath, whether it is another layer of dried paint, or the canvas or board itself. Here a thick layer of blue paint has been applied with a painting knife, and the blade of the knife then used as the drawing instrument. You can use all kinds of tools for this technique; a screwdriver, for instance, will give a line similar to that made by drawing with a carpenter's pencil. Many artists whittle the end of an old paintbrush for sgraffito effects as the softer wood is less likely to damage the canvas.

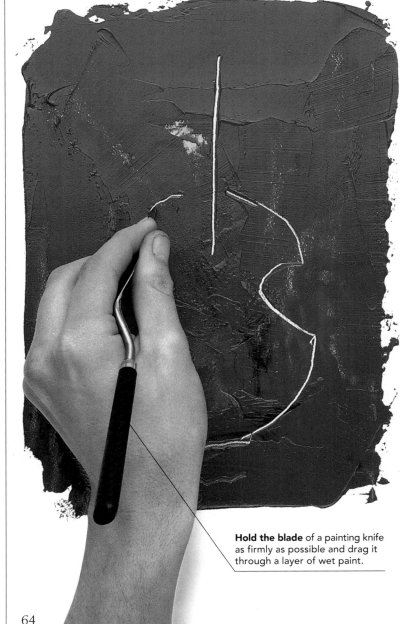

Hold the blade of a painting knife as firmly as possible and drag it through a layer of wet paint.

OIL STICKS

Oil sticks are a type of oil paint blended with waxes and applied directly on to the canvas. You can dispense with brushes entirely, modifying colours with a piece of cloth or a finger. Oil sticks are unlike other drawing materials in that they are extremely creamy in texture. They are good for working wet-in-wet, so you can apply one wet colour over another without making a muddy mixture. In this study of a carnival mask, the background has been rubbed with a cloth dipped in turpentine and the other colours left unmodified.

Use a tape with a low tack adhesive, such as masking tape or drafting tape.

Masking tape
If you want to paint a very straight edge, use masking tape. Ensure that the tape has a low tack adhesive and that the paint is dry before you apply it. Pull the tape away carefully, or it may pull off the paint beneath.

Modifying a painted surface
Modify the surface of an oil painting if you want to remove excess colour, or adapt the overall effect. One method, which is also a form of monoprinting, is to lay a sheet of paper over an area of paint, rub it gently with your hand, and pull it off slowly. Use a damp, absorbent paper if you want to remove plenty of paint.

If you want to make a monoprint, paint an image on a slab of glass and take a print of it using absorbent paper.

VARNISHING & FRAMING

A FILM OF VARNISH PROTECTS an oil work from atmospheric pollution and abrasion. A gloss varnish can also bring out the colours in a work, giving them a greater saturation and depth, and so heightening the impact of the picture. A varnish is actually a solution of resin in a solvent, and the resin forms a hard but flexible protective film after the solvent has evaporated.

A frame can have a significant impact on a work, giving it a focus that can either detract from its appearance, or allow it to be seen at its best. You should choose a frame with care and decide whether you make it yourself or have it made professionally; the appearance of a painting can easily be ruined by a badly made frame with its corners out of alignment.

Choosing a frame
A frame can alter the look of a painting quite significantly, so try to choose from a wide selection of frame samples.

Materials

Cotton wool

Varnish

Flat bristle brush

Tape measure

Varnishing

A painting should be completely dry before varnishing, so it is advisable to leave it for about three months. You can make an acceptable varnish by dissolving dammar resin in turpentine, but most artists buy a good quality dammar varnish for a high gloss look, or ketone varnish for a less yellowing effect. The painting must also be free from dust, dirt, and grease, which can cause the varnish to form a blotchy surface. Make sure the room you choose to work in is well ventilated and warm.

1 ▲ Lay your dry painting on a flat surface and clean it with cotton wool moistened with saliva – an excellent cleaning agent. This should ensure that the painting is completely clear of dust and grease.

2 ◀ Apply a coat of varnish with a flat bristle brush (you can buy special varnishing brushes from artists' suppliers), making parallel strokes in one direction across the painting. When the first layer of varnish is dry, apply a second coat with the same varnishing brush, working at right angles to the first coat. This produces a fine, even film of varnish.

Framing

It can be hard to produce a well made frame so if you feel at all unsure about making your own, use a professional framemaker. Choose a frame that best suits the style of your painting.

If the work is bright and vigorously painted, choose a bold, simple frame.

1 ◀ Measure the height and width of the painting with a tape measure. You should be as precise as possible so that the frame can then be cut to fit the painting exactly.

2 ▶ The measurements of the painting form the inside lengths of the frame, so measure off the correct height and width on four pieces of moulding and cut 45 degree angles at either end. You can use a special mitre cutter, but this is an expensive piece of equipment, so a simple mitre box is a good alternative (*right*). Fit a tenon saw into the prepared grooves of the mitre box and cut the required angle in the wood.

3 ◀ Spread a special wood glue over the sawn edges of two pieces of moulding to form one corner of the frame. This needs to be held firmly in place until the glue has dried, so use a corner clamp to hold the pieces of wood in a rigid position.

4 ▶ Tap in panel pins on either side of the corner with a hammer, and then drive the pins right into the wood using a nail punch.

6 ◀ Finally, seal the back of the frame and cover all the panel pins using gum strip around the edges.

5 ▲ Once all four corners have been secured, place the painting in the frame, cut out a piece of hardboard the same size as the painting, and slot it in the back. Drive in some more panel pins to tighten the board.

Changing the look of a painting
This work is shown with two different mouldings to illustrate how a frame changes the shape and look of a painting. Choose certain colours or textures to enhance a painting. Avoid brightly coloured frames for subtle, low-key paintings.

Materials

Mitre box

Tenon saw

Wood glue

Hammer

Panel pins

Nail punch

Gum strip

Hardboard

Moulding

GLOSSARY

ADJACENT COLOURS Those colours literally closest to each other on the colour wheel; also used to describe colours that lie next to one another in a painting. Adjacent complementary colours appear brighter together because each reinforces the effect of the other.

ADVANCING COLOUR The perception of a colour, usually warm (orange-red), as being close to the viewer.

AERIAL PERSPECTIVE This describes the effect of atmospheric conditions on our perception of the tone and colour of distant objects. As objects recede towards the horizon they appear lighter in tone and more blue due to the scattering of light in the atmosphere. Artists tend to use a cool colour such as blue to paint objects viewed in the distance to achieve a sense of space. Some artists like to work from the palest tones through to the darkest tones in the foreground to create distance and depth. This principle is used particularly in landscape painting.

ALLA PRIMA Literally means "at first" and is a direct form of painting made in one session or while the colours remain wet. (As opposed to "indirect" painting in which the painting is built up in layers). This is the technique employed by artists when they want to paint spontaneously. It is, however, a difficult style to master as it requires fluent brushstrokes and a skilful manipulation of the paint.

BINDER In a paint, this is the substance which holds the pigment particles together and which acts as an adhesive to the support (*see also* extender).

BLENDING A soft, gradual transition from one colour or tone to another. A clean dry brush should be used to make gentle strokes in the same direction to join separate colours. Blending may involve slightly softening the sharp outline of a single object against a background, or working on the whole painting, so that it takes on a rounded, seemingly three-dimensional effect.

BRISTLE BRUSHES Hog hair bristle brushes are used extensively in oil painting. They have coarse hairs which hold plenty of thick paint and yet retain their shape. Bristle brushes are useful for covering large areas with a uniform tone and for blending.

BROKEN COLOUR Colour that has been broken up by mixing with another colour or affected optically by the juxtaposition or superimposition of another colour. Broken colour can be created using a dry brush or scumbling technique.

CHALK Natural calcium carbonate, used in the preparation of chalk/glue grounds for its whiteness and opacity and as a cheap extender in oil-based paints in which it is translucent. "Chalking" is the powdering of the paint surface due to the breakdown of the binder as a result of ultraviolet radiation.

CHARCOAL Carbonized wood made by charring willow, vine, or other twigs in airtight containers. Charcoal is one of the oldest drawing materials. If charcoal is used for a preparatory drawing, the excess dust can be rubbed off the surface using a large soft hair brush or a piece of doughy bread.

CHROMA The intensity or saturation of a colour. Chromatic is the term used for an image that has been drawn or painted in a range of different colours.

COLOUR TEMPERATURE A measurement of colour in degrees Kelvin. This is also of importance to photographers who need to correlate the colour temperature of a light source with the type of film they use. As artists we are aware that the colour temperature of a room illuminated by electric light is significantly different from (yellower than) that of daylight.

COMPLEMENTARY COLOUR Two colours of maximum contrast opposite one another on the colour wheel. The complementary of a primary colour is the combination of the two remaining primary colours. For example, the complementary of blue is orange-red, the opposite of red is green, and the complement of yellow is violet.

COOL COLOUR Generally, a colour such as blue is considered cool. Distant colours appear bluer due to atmospheric effects, so cool colours are therefore said to recede.

DAMMAR A soft resin soluble in turpentine and used to make a gloss varnish. You can make an acceptable varnish by dissolving some dammar resin in a jar of turpentine or white spirit.

DARKS Those parts of a painting that are in shadow.

DIRECT PAINTING *See* alla prima.

DRAGGED Describes brushstrokes that are made across the textured surface of canvas or paint or at a shallow angle into wet paint.

Sgraffito

Drawing grid

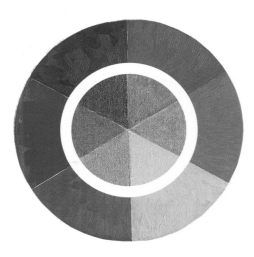
Colour wheel

DRAWING GRID A drawing grid is made up of a series of squares that enable an artist to transfer a sketch proportionately on to a large scale support. The grid can easily be produced by drawing squares on to a piece of acetate or tracing paper which is then laid over the sketch.

DRY BRUSH TECHNIQUE A method of painting in which paint of a dry or stiff consistency is stroked or rubbed across the canvas. It is picked up on the ridges of the canvas or by the texture of paint on the surface, leaving some of the colour on the canvas still visible and producing a broken colour effect (*see also* scumbling).

EASEL A frame for holding a painting while the artist works on it. Landscape painters tend to use sketching easels which are of a light construction. A good sketching easel allows the painting to be held securely in any position from vertical to horizontal. The heavy radial studio easel and vertical studio easel are suitable for studio work.

EXTENDER A pigment which has a limited effect on a colour. It may be added to control the properties of a paint or to reduce the cost. Examples are chalk and china clay.

High-key colour

Low-key colour

FAT-OVER-LEAN The rule applying to oil painting in layers, in which each superimposed layer should have a little more oil in the paint than the one beneath. This ensures that each layer is more flexible as a dried film than the one below it, with less risk of the paint cracking.

FERRULE The metal part of a brush which surrounds and retains the hairs.

FIXATIVE A surface coating which prevents charcoal, chalk, and conté crayon from becoming dusty and from mixing with overlaid colour.

FLAT COLOUR An area of matt colour of uniform tone and hue.

FUGITIVE Colours which are not lightfast and will fade over a period of time.

GESSO A traditional ground for tempera and oil painting on panel comprising animal glue (rabbit skin glue) and plaster of paris. In northern Europe chalk and glue were used for the same purpose. Not to be confused with the product acrylic gesso (primer) which is also commonly available as a primer for acrylic painting.

GLAZE A film of transparent or translucent oil colour laid over another dried colour or underpainting. The oil paint is usually mixed with an oil painting medium to make it more malleable.

GROUND The surface on which colour is applied. This is usually the coating rather than the support. A coloured ground is useful for low-key paintings where the ground provides the half tones and the unifying element for the different colours. A coloured ground can also be applied as an imprimatura, or as a primer that has been coloured.

HALF TONES Transitional tones between the highlights and the darks.

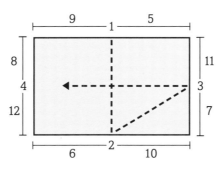
Stretching a canvas

HATCHING Making tonal gradations by shading with long thin brushstrokes. Often used in underpainting.

HEEL OF BRUSH The base of the hairs near the ferrule.

HIGH-KEY COLOUR Brilliant and saturated colour. Some oil colours, especially the transparent ones, are dark when used directly from the tube, so a little white can be mixed with them to give a saturated colour effect. Alternatively, such colours can be used thinly on a white ground for a similar high-key look. High-key paintings are usually painted on white or near-white grounds.

HIGHLIGHT The lightest tone in drawing or painting. In oil painting techniques, white constitutes the lightest tone.

HUE Describes the actual colour of an object or substance. Its hue may be red, yellow, blue, green, and so on.

IMPASTO A thick layer of paint, often applied with a painting knife or a bristle brush, which is heaped up in ridges to create a heavily textured surface and a look of fresh immediacy. Artists often scrape the paint off the surface of the support and apply the colour again if it does not retain the crispness of the effect required.

IMPRIMATURA A thin overall film or stain of translucent colour over a white priming. This is applied before the artist begins to paint. It does not affect the reflective qualities of the ground, but it provides a useful background colour and makes it easier to paint between the lights and darks. It also allows for an economical style.

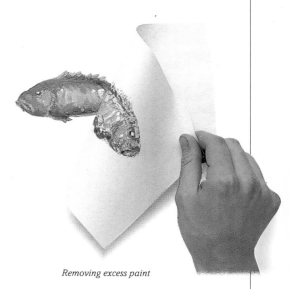
Removing excess paint

LAY IN The initial painting stage over a preliminary drawing where the colours are applied as broad areas of flat colour. This technique is also known as blocking in.

LIGHTFASTNESS The permanence or durability of a colour.

LINSEED OIL A vegetable drying oil from the seeds of the flax plant used as a binding material in oil colour. Linseed oil is the most commonly used of oils and it dries more quickly than "semi-drying" oils. The oil does not dry by evaporation but forms a solid film.

LOW-KEY COLOUR Subdued, unsaturated colour that tends towards brown and grey. Tertiary colours are low-key in appearance and produce neutral hues similar in mood and tone.

MAHL STICK A bamboo or aluminium stick about 4ft (1.25m) long with a ball-shaped end. If you paint with your right hand the stick is held with the left hand, with the ball end touching the canvas so that the right hand can rest on the stick while painting. This helps you to work with a steadier hand if you need to work on a particular area.

MASKING TAPE Pressure-sensitive tape used to protect areas from paint.

MEDIUM The binding material or "vehicle" for pigment in a paint system. In oil paint a vegetable drying oil such as linseed oil is the medium. An oil painting medium is used to modify the consistency of oil paint in techniques such as glazing. A typical oil painting medium is made up of a mixture of stand oil (linseed oil that has been boiled) and turpentine.

MONOPRINT A unique print taken from a work created on a slab of glass or laminate.

OIL STICKS A type of oil paint blended with waxes in the form of sticks and applied directly on to the canvas. Colours can be modified with a piece of cloth or a finger. Oil sticks, unlike other drawing materials, are extremely creamy in texture and are good for working wet-in-wet.

OPAQUE PAINTING Paintings that use predominantly opaque paints and the techniques associated with them.

OPTICAL MIX When a colour is arrived at by the visual effect of overlaying or abutting distinct colours, rather than by physically mixing them on a palette.

PERSPECTIVE The method of representing a three-dimensional object on a two-dimensional surface. Linear perspective makes objects appear smaller as they get further away by means of a geometric system of measurement.

PHTHALOCYANINE Modern organic transparent blue and green (chlorinated copper phthalocyanine) pigments of high tinting strengths and excellent lightfastness. Also known by trade names.

PHYSICAL MIX When a colour is created by pre-mixing two or more colours together on the palette before application to the support. Wet-in-wet and wet-on-dry techniques refer to mixing paints on the support itself.

PIGMENT A solid coloured material in the form of discrete particles which forms the basic component of all types of paint. In oil painting, pigments are bound together with a semi-drying or drying oil, such as linseed oil. Pigments come in different forms and the amount of oil used to coat each type of pigment will vary.

PLEIN AIR This term refers to painting in the open air. Alla prima techniques are normally used in this situation.

PRIMARY COLOURS The three colours of red, blue, and yellow in painting that cannot be produced by mixing any other colours.

PRIMING This refers to the preliminary coating laid on to the support prior to painting. A layer of priming protects the support from any potentially damaging components of paint and provides the surface with the right key, absorbency, and colour before painting.

RECEDING COLOUR The perception of a colour, usually a cool (blue), as being distant from the viewer.

REFRACTIVE INDEX A measure of the degree of refraction of a substance. The ratio between the angle of the incident ray in air with that of the refracted ray in the substance produces this measure.

SGRAFFITO A technique, usually involving a scalpel or a sharp knife, in which dried paint is scraped off the painted surface so that the colour of the surface, or a dry colour painted previously, is visible. This is often used for textural effects.

SABLE BRUSH Mink tail hair used to make fine brushes. Normally used in watercolour techniques but which can also be used in oil painting for fine detailed brushwork or final touches and highlights.

SATURATION The degree of intensity of a colour. Colours can be saturated i.e. vivid and of intense hue, or unsaturated i.e. dull, tending towards grey.

SCUMBLING A painting technique in which semi-opaque or thin opaque colours are

Alla prima

Viewfinder

Ready-primed canvas

loosely brushed over an underpainted area so that patches of the colour beneath show through.

SECONDARY COLOURS The colours arrived at by mixing two primaries i.e. blue and yellow make green, red and yellow make orange, and red and blue make violet. However, if different proportions of each primary colour are combined, a range of tones of the secondary colour can be produced.

SHADE Colour mixed with black.

SIZE Rabbit skin or other glue used to protect canvas from the potentially damaging effects of oil in the paint before priming and to seal or reduce the absorbency of wooden panels. The binding material for gesso.

SOFT HAIR BRUSHES These are used mainly in watercolour painting but are also suitable for precise brushwork in oil painting. They can hold a great deal of thin paint while still retaining their shape.

STRETCHER The wooden frame on which a canvas is stretched.

SUPPORT The material on which a painting is made. Almost any surface can be used, but artists tend to use either a wooden panel or a canvas to work on. These materials are available in a range of textures and weights.

TERTIARY COLOUR A colour that contains a proportion of each of the three primaries (*see also* unsaturated colour).

TINT Colour mixed with white. "Tinting strength" is the strength of a particular colour or pigment.

TONE The degree of darkness or lightness of a colour. Crumpling a piece of white paper allows you to see a range of tonal contrast.

TONED GROUND Also called a coloured ground. An opaque layer of coloured paint of uniform tone applied over the priming before starting the painting.

TRANSPARENT PAINTING A painting technique that relies on the transparency of the paints used.

TURPENTINE (DISTILLED) Used to thin oil colour and to make resin varnishes such as dammar varnish. Turpentine is also used as an ingredient in a number of oil painting mediums. White spirit can be used instead of turpentine.

UNSATURATED COLOUR Sometimes known as desaturated colour. A pure, saturated colour becomes unsaturated when mixed with another colour into a tint or a shade. When three colours are mixed together in unequal amounts, the resultant colour can be called a coloured neutral.

VALUE The extent to which a colour reflects or transmits light.

VARNISH Protective surface over a finished painting imparting a glossy or matt surface appearance to a painting.

VIEWFINDER A rectangular hole to the scale of the artist's support cut in a small piece of cardboard to act as a framing device. This is held up at arm's length so that the scene to be drawn or painted can be viewed through it and the most pleasing composition can be found.

VISCOSITY A measure of the flow characteristic of a colour or medium (e.g. stand oil is more viscous than alkali-refined linseed oil). Oil paint with some viscosity is described as having body.

WARM COLOUR Generally, a colour such as orange-red is considered warm. In accordance with atmospheric or aerial perspective, warm colours appear to advance towards the viewer.

WET-IN-WET Working with wet paint into wet paint on the surface of the support.

WET-ON-DRY Applying a layer of wet paint on to a dry surface.

Proportion of oil to pigment

A NOTE ON COLOURS, PIGMENTS AND TOXICITY

In recommending Winsor Blue and Winsor Green (which are trade names of the Winsor & Newton Company) we are recommending "Phthalocyanine" pigments; other artists' material manufacturers refer to them by their own trade names. These include Phthalo Blue and Green, Monestial Blue and Green and so on. Similarly, in recommending Permanent Rose we are recommending a "Quinacridone" pigment. If you have any doubts about which pigment you are buying, refer to the manufacturer's literature.

We have tried to avoid recommending pigments, such as the Chrome colours, which carry a significant health risk. Toxic pigments such as Lead White or Cobalt Blue should also be avoided when making your own colours. In the case of colours such as the Cadmiums, however, there is nothing commercially available which matches them for colour and permanence. But there is no danger in their use nor in that of other pigments provided artists take sensible precautions.

Solvents are damaging to your health, so always keep the lids of solvent jars screwed on tight and use only as much as you need. The long-term effects from inhaling the fumes of distilled turpentine and white spirit include loss of memory, the inability to follow an argument, and paranoia.

A NOTE ON BRUSHES

The brush sizes given here refer to Winsor & Newton brushes. They may vary slightly from those of other manufacturers.

Bristle brushes

Protective case

Working on a white ground

INDEX

ACKNOWLEDGEMENTS

Author's acknowledgements
Ray Smith would like to thank Alun Foster at Winsor & Newton Ltd. for his expert advice. Thank you also to the many artists who agreed to allow their paintings to enrich the book and to The Royal Academy for providing valuable assistance. Special thanks to everyone at Dorling Kindersley associated with the DK Art School project and in particular to my editor, Susannah Steel, for her lively and enthusiastic commitment to the text, and to Heather McCarry, whose flair and judgement in the design shines through the pages. Thank you also to Margaret Chang for her great help with the picture research.

Picture credits
Key: *t*=top, *b*=bottom, *c*=centre, *l*=left, *r*=right *a/w*=artworks

Endpapers: Jane Gifford; *pp8/9:* van Eyck, Rembrandt, Ruysch, Tura, reproduced by courtesy of the Trustees, The National Gallery, London; Titian, Isabella Stewart Gardner Museum, Boston; *pp10/11:* Claude, reproduced by courtesy of the Trustees, The National Gallery, London; Monet, The Brooklyn Museum 20.634 Gift of A. Augustus Healy; Cézanne, Louvre/Réunion des Musées Nationaux; O'Keeffe, Collection of the University of Arizona Museum of Art, Gift of Oliver James, ©1993 The Georgia O'Keeffe Foundation/ARS, New York; ©Richter, Anthony d'Offay Gallery; *pp16/17:* all, Ray Smith; *pp22/23:* Chagall, Kunsthalle Museum, Hamburg, ADAGP, Paris and DACS, London 1993; ©Gore RA, ©Sutton RA, Royal Academy of Arts Library; *p26: bl* Ray Smith; *r* Jane Gifford; *p27: t* Jane Gifford; *b* Ray Smith; *p28 t* Jane Gifford; *b* Ray Smith; *p29 t* Jane Gifford; *b* Ray Smith; *pp32/33:* ©Levene RA, Royal Academy of Arts Library; Frampton, all rights reserved/The Tate Gallery, London, Nolde, Staatdgalerie,

Stuttgart, ©Nolde-Stiftung Seebüll/Arthothek Kunstdia-Archiv; *p35 tl* Ray Smith; *tr, br* Trevor Chamberlain; *bl* Lance Beeke; *pp38/39* all, Ian McCaughrean; *pp40/41 a/w,* Jane Gifford; *pp44/45:* Kokoschka, Albright Knox, Atkins Museum/Visual Arts Library ©DACS 1993; ©Jacklin RA, ©Weight RA, ©Philipson RA, The Royal Academy of Arts Library; *pp50/51:* Hamilton-Fraser RA, Rooney RA, Royal Academy of Arts Library; Picasso, Private Collection/Visual Arts Library; ©DACS 1993; *pp56/57:* van Gogh, Musée d'Orsay, Paris; Monet, reproduced by courtesy of the Trustees, The National Gallery, London; ©Howard RA, ©Dunstan RA, Royal Academy of Arts Library; Schnabel, Courtesy of Galerie Bruno Bischofberger, Zurich, all rights reserved; *pp62/63:* Moroni, The National Gallery of Ireland; El Greco, Metropolitan Museum of Art, New York/Visual Arts Library; *p64:* Ian McCaughrean; *p65: tl* Ray Smith; rest Ian McCaughrean.

Dorling Kindersley would like to thank: Paintworks, Cornellison & Son Ltd, and Winsor & Newton for kindly supplying the artists' materials used in the book.